Science

ROB JOHNSEY

TEACHER
TIMESAVERS

Published by Scholastic Ltd,
Villiers House,
Clarendon Avenue,
Leamington Spa,
Warwickshire CV32 5PR

© **1994 Scholastic Ltd**
Text © 1994 Rob Johnsey
New edition 1995
3 4 5 6 7 8 9   7 8 9 0 1 2 3 4 5

Author Rob Johnsey
Editor Jo Saxelby-Jennings
Assistant editor Joanne Boden
Series designer Joy White
Illustrations Sally Alexander and Jenny Tulip
Cover illustration Frances Lloyd
Cover photograph Martyn Chillmaid

Designed using Aldus Pagemaker
Processed by Pages Bureau, Leamington Spa
Artwork by Liz Preece, Castle Graphics, Kenilworth
Printed in Great Britain by Ebenezer Baylis & Son, Worcester

British Library Cataloguing-in-Publication Data
A catalogue record for this book is
available from the British Library.

ISBN 0-590-53533-1 2nd revised edition
(ISBN 0-590-53084-4 1st edition)

Contents

Introduction

Primary science is an Aladdin's cave full of sparkling experiences and discoveries made by children as they learn through practical tasks. Effective teachers are those who can draw upon a range of exciting and relevant science activities at the appropriate times. This book represents one casket of treasures, which can be used by busy classroom teachers in a variety of ways:

- as an initial stimulus for scientific activities and investigations;
- as extension work for a science activity;
- as a bank of ideas for the teacher to adapt to suit his or her own style of teaching;
- as work to take home and share with parents.
  Primary science is essentially about learning through practical activity. These activities range from those which involve following instructions from the teacher to those in which the children plan and execute their own investigations.

Experimental and Investigative Science

This special attainment target describes the skills children need to investigate in a scientific way. They should learn to take more and more responsibility for planning and carrying out these investigations using their existing scientific knowledge. The activity sheets, therefore, do not say *how* to carry out an investigation. It is for them to plan and execute it with the help of discussions with the teacher and other children.

The photocopiable sheets

The activities in this book do not form a complete scheme of work for science. The pages have been arranged under typical primary school topic headings and placed in approximate order of difficulty within each section. However, you are quite likely to find ideas for a topic on 'Ourselves' under 'Measuring skills' or 'Forces'. The activities are not linked to a particular key stage or National Curriculum level – this is for you to decide when fitting the activity into an overall plan. Some activities could take you into Key Stage 3 for those children ready for it. Attainment targets from the England and Wales National Curriculum which the activities support are given in the notes. Attainment outcomes from the Scottish 5-14 Guidelines relevant to the book are Understanding Living Things and the Processes of Life, Understanding Energy and Forces, and Understanding Earth and Space. See the inside back cover for details of Northern Ireland Curriculum links.

Some of the activity sheets need to be supported by simple apparatus and may provide the stimulus for further investigations. Many of the sheets, however, can be completed as paper and pencil tasks only. These can be used as supporting material for practical tasks. Some of the pages will be used once, while others may be used over again in various ways. The following notes give suggestions for getting the most out of each activity. Warning symbols indicate where special care should be taken. ❑ indicates extension work.

Ourselves

Looking at eyes (Sc2) This activity focuses on the skill of observation. The children could make drawings, paintings or collages of their eye observations. Identifying similarities and differences is an important skill to emphasise.
❑ The children could carry out a similar task observing noses, ears, mouths and so on.

The sense of smell (Sc1, 2) The children should learn to observe in their investigations using as many of their senses as possible. A smell quiz will encourage them to use a sense they may take for granted. This activity illustrates how observations can be focused if much of the extra stimulus around is suppressed.

Big ears (Sc1, 2, 4) This hearing test must be carried out in a quiet room. It may not be possible to get consistent results, but it is important that the test is carried out in a fair way.
❑ Can the children devise their own hearing test?

Touch test (Sc1, 2) There are obvious links between this activity and the use of Braille. The strip could be traced on to scrap paper or the children could make a similar one with their own patterns. Remind them about the potential dangers of using drawing pins!
❑ Can the children devise their own touch test using paper clips bent into different patterns? They might ask their partners to try to draw the paper clips without looking at them.

Fingerprints (Sc2) Discuss the subtle differences between the four categories of fingerprint (whorl, loop, arch and composite) with the children before they begin their classification. The prints on the sheet are real ones and may not fit exactly into each category.
❑ Can the children 'lift' fingerprints by shaking chalk dust or talc on to the print, blowing away the excess and lifting what remains with a length of transparent sticky tape?

False teeth (Sc2) This model enables children to get a clearer picture of a part of themselves they rarely see. Compare the cutting action of the incisors with the grinding action of the molars.

Joints (Sc2) These model parts could be cut out, stuck on to card and fitted together, using a hole punch to make clean holes. Alternatively, the parts could be copied directly on to card. The model can be used: to discuss body joints; as a starting point for designing model furniture; or for a model fashion parade.

❏ Can the children make a similar model of a jointed hand, including the fingers and wrist?

The body (Sc2) This body outline could be used in a variety of ways: for drawing on clothes and naming them; for cutting out clothes shapes and 'dressing' the model; for naming external body parts; for drawing a skeleton inside; or in conjunction with page 23.

Inside our bodies (Sc2) Some of the bones and internal organs of the body are illustrated here. The children could cut these out and stick them in the correct positions on the body outline on page 22. The parts could then be labelled and their functions discussed.

Measuring people: 1 (Sc1, 2) One of the skills required in Sc1 is that children learn to select the most appropriate instrument when making measurements. This sheet encourages them to do this while measuring parts of their bodies.

Measuring people: 2 (Sc1, 2) Here the children are encouraged to analyse/ask questions about the data they have gathered. One way of finding answers is to look for patterns in graphs. For example, the correlation between the variables height and head circumference can be seen on the simple scattergraph below:

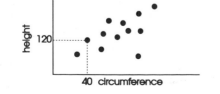

❏ Can the children pose similar questions to answer in the same way? For example, do children with wide handspans have the thickest wrists?

How big are your lungs? (Sc2) This activity enables children to get an approximate idea of the capacity of their lungs. It might complement a maths activity on volume. The polythene bag must be a small one which is filled a number of times from completely full lungs. The children may need help to understand that they must exhale, hold their breath, empty the bag and exhale again until their lungs are empty. They *must* be warned about the dangers of playing with polythene bags and those with breathing difficulties should not attempt this activity.

Exercise and breathing (Sc2) The children will need help and practice in counting the number of breaths taken in one minute. Those who are doing the breathing can help in this by making some kind of small movement as they breathe in. This investigation should show that breathing rate increases during exercise and gradually decreases afterwards.

❏ The children could carry out a similar investigation by measuring pulse rate.

Measuring lung capacity (Sc2) The children may need help with filling the bottle by submerging it and then raising it vertically with the neck still under the water. If the bottle is a large one (3 litres) then there may be no need to refill the bottle with water half way through the activity. The children may also need help in understanding how to measure the volume of the air remaining in the bottle.

Animals

Minibeasts 1 and 2, Sea creatures, Freshwater creatures and Birds 1 and 2 (Sc2) These sheets can be used in a variety of ways.

• The eight cards on each page (animal and its name) can be cut out and the pictures coloured using the correct natural colours, which may be found from reference books.

• The cards can be used for simple classification; for example, 'Minibeasts 1 and 2' could be grouped into: Animals with legs/Animals without legs; Animals with wings/ Animals without wings; Insects/Not insects; Live in soil/Live on leaves/Other;

• A branching key can be produced for any collection of animals. (See pages 44 and 45.)

• The following games can be played if a duplicate set of cards is produced:

Snap – cards are shared out and held face down. Each player reveals one card at a time until two consecutive cards are the same. The first player to call, 'Snap!' wins the cards in the pile.

Pairs (Pelmanism) – cards are spread out, face down on a table. Players take turns to turn over two cards. If these are the same they are won, if they are different they are turned back over.

• The cards can be cut out, folded along the dotted line and pasted back-to-back. Then the children can try to name each animal and check by turning over the card. Alternatively, they can describe the animal once they have read its name and turn over to check they were right.

• The animal pictures can be cut from the names, the cards jumbled up and rematched. The game, 'Pairs' (described above) can be played by matching animals and names.

• Broader classification can take place by mixing the cards from all the sheets.

Identifying minibeasts (Sc2) This is a simple key which can be used to identify the animals around the page. The children should choose a minibeast on the page and then answer the

questions until it has been identified.
Answers: a=harvestman; b=stag beetle; c=honey-bee; d=slug; e=centipede; f=earthworm; g=ant; h=damselfly; i=bumble-bee; j=housefly; k=millipede.

❑ The children might like to make their own keys based on a small collection of, for example, cutlery, LEGO components or school books.

Minibeast habitats (Sc2) This page might support classroom work on habitats. Some preliminary work on exploring real habitats is necessary. The animals are grouped so that the answers should be clear.

❑ The children might explore the habitats illustrated on the sheet and add drawings of their own of new animals found in these habitats.

Describing habitats (Sc2) Each animal habitat has its own peculiar characteristics which make it suitable for a particular set of animals. Children can be made more aware of these characteristics by describing them in a record chart. At the same time they should be aware that animals don't live just anywhere, but choose to live where conditions suit them.

Food chains (Sc2) The concept of a food chain should be discussed with the children before they attempt this sheet. What happens if a food chain is broken or disturbed? Discuss the children's answers once they have finished.

❑ Are there any food chains involving humans?

The Daily Croaker **(Sc2)** This task encourages the children to think about the impact humans have on the natural environment. The article describes the effect of depriving a frog population of its spawning pond and the positive effects of creating garden ponds. This exercise could be carried out with the help of a word processor or desk top publishing package.

Answers: 3=c, 4=e, 5=h, 6=d, 7=b, 8=g, 9=f, 10=a.

❑ Can the children write their own newspaper article on a similar theme? Can they jumble up their stories for others to correct?

Growing plants

Parts of a buttercup (Sc2) This sheet will help the children reinforce their knowledge of the simple parts of a flower, where it grows and how the parts function. It is important that they begin to understand that a plant makes its own food in its leaves by using sunlight, water, minerals and gases (carbon dioxide) from the air. The soil provides the minerals and water and a safe anchorage for most plants, but is not their source of food.

Parts of plants (Sc2) This sheet will help the children understand that while many plants have roots, stems, flowers and so on these can take different forms.

Watching and recording runner beans grow (Sc2) Use this page to record the progress of a runner bean as it grows between a glass jar and damp paper. The children can make a record every few days depending on the growth rate. They can expect to observe the growth of the main and lateral roots, then the shoot, and then the emergence of a number of leaves.

Sorting fruit (Sc2) This activity will enable the children to think about sorting fruit into sets. The first two sets have an overlap (intersection) and should provide an opportunity to talk about fruit whose skin and seeds are eaten (tomato and possibly grapes). The second sorting exercise enables children to think about subsets and those fruits excluded from a set.

Identifying fruit (Sc2) This page will enable children to investigate a branching key. They should choose one fruit at a time and answer

the questions about it until it can be placed in one of the boxes.

Identifying leaves: 1 (Sc2) This is a simple introduction to identifying natural objects using a branching key and could be used in conjunction with page 44, 'Identifying fruit'.

Eating plants (Sc2) *Answers*: flower = cauliflower, broccoli; stem = celery, rhubarb; leaf = lettuce, cabbage, thyme; fruit = apple, tomato, orange, cucumber; seed = peas, sweetcorn, broadbean; root = carrot, radish.

❑ The children can add foods of their own to the lists; for example, rice, flour, pear, baked beans.

Making food from plants (Sc2) Many children will not be aware that chocolate is made from the cocoa bean and cornflakes from sweetcorn.

❑ The children might also link the food products with their countries of origin.

Parts of a flowering plant (Sc2) You may feel that some of this vocabulary is too advanced for the children and may wish to mask out some of the words. Each word needed is given, but may need to be used more than once.

Identifying leaves: 2 (Sc2) This page gives children the chance to use a conventional key for identifying some common leaves. *Answers* a= oak, b=ash, c=hazel, d=sycamore, e=elm, f=beech, g=hawthorn, h=laburnum.

Forces

Making forces (Sc4) This series of activities will help children to identify the common forces around them as simple pushes or pulls. They may also begin to think about the size of the forces. Most, but not all, of the forces illustrated produce some kind of movement. Where a force does not move something it is being balanced out by other forces, for example, as in the force on the rope and the force on the classroom wall.

Muscles and forces (Sc4) Muscles produce forces by expanding and shortening. The force produced moves a part of the body – in this case, the foot. In the model, each elastic band can be made to move the foot by pulling it outwards.

Similar muscles are found in the upper arm (the biceps and triceps) and these move the lower arm up and down.
❏ The children could try to make another model to represent the arm or upper and lower leg.

Marbles and moving air (Sc4) 'Movement' and 'force' are often confused. They are quite separate things, but are interrelated. A force is required to start a movement or stop it. This activity enables children to think about the forces on a marble and how these move it, slow it down or change its direction. In this instance, the force is provided by the moving air from the straw, but could equally be provided by a finger.

Measuring forces (Sc1, 4) The children can make their own force meter and measure some common forces. The stretch in an elastic band is measured against an arbitrary scale and indicates the size of the force.

What do forces do? (Sc4) We cannot see a force, but we can observe its effect. Be clear that the effects we are looking for are only on the shaded part of each picture and in most cases, there are at least *two* forces acting. For instance, the nail (picture 3) has gravity and magnetic force acting on it, while the box (picture 8) has the person pushing it and friction with the floor.

Magnetic force (Sc1, 4) This activity shows just one way of measuring magnetic force. The scale should be pinned up vertically – perhaps temporarily on part of a classroom notice board. Experiment with the size of the Plasticine. Help the children to devise a table for their results.

Force meters: 1 (Sc4) This sheet could be used alongside a real force meter to give practice in reading the scale. *Answers*: 3N, 9N, 1N, 5N, 3.5N, 10N.

Force meters: 2 (Sc4) This is similar to the previous sheet (page 56) but is more of a challenge because it involves reading decimal parts on the scales. *Answers*: 5N, 4.5N, 3.2N, 0.5N, 21N, 0.6N, 11N, 0.3N, 0.7N, 7N.

Water can push (Sc4) Whether an object floats or sinks depends on the balance of forces on it. When an object is placed in water there are two forces involved: (i) the force of gravity called its 'weight' (acting downwards), and (ii) the force of the water called 'upthrust' (acting upwards). If the downward force is greatest the object sinks and vice versa. This activity should show that even objects which sink still experience upthrust.

Bouncing balls (Sc1, 4) When a ball hits the ground, and is ready to bounce back up, both the ball and the ground are being squashed at that moment. When they both spring back into shape the combined force moves the ball upwards. Think about the forces on a falling and bouncing ball. Then ask the children to investigate the bounciness of different surfaces by carrying out a fair test.

Friction – friend or foe? (Sc4) Friction is an important force which tries to oppose movement. This can be both useful, for example, when it prevents us sliding down a slope, and a nuisance, when we have to pedal harder due to a poorly-oiled bicycle. The pictures which show friction as a nuisance are: sledging down a slope, friction on a bicycle crank and the space capsule overheating. In some of the diagrams friction may be both helpful and unhelpful.

Bicycle gears (Sc4) You will need access to a bicycle with gears for this activity. When the pedal is pulled down the force is just overcoming the friction in all the moving parts. As subsequent gears are tried it will be found that the lower gears allow a smaller force to move the wheel.

Energy and moving things

Energy can be dangerous (Sc4) This sheet could be a stimulus for group work where the children discuss the dangers shown in the pictures and then make a poster based on dangerous energy. Help them to identify the energy involved in each case so that they do not merely describe the picture. *Answers:* 1=sound energy, 2=radiant energy, 3=movement energy, 4=raised energy (ability of something to fall), 5=heat energy, 6=electrical energy.

Booby trap (Sc1, 4) This activity gives children a chance to investigate using a varying energy source. The task provides a context in which to discuss energy and how it might be controlled. Warn them about flying matchsticks in these traps.
❏ Encourage the children to make other devices which use energy from a twisted elastic band such as a cotton reel roller, or a paddle boat.

Toy car on a slope (Sc1, 4) The toy car can possess different amounts of raised (potential) energy depending from where it is released on the slope. How far the car rolls from the bottom of the slope is a measure of that initial energy. As the car rolls down the slope some of the energy is changed into sound and heat (through friction), but most is changed into movement. This movement energy is eventually changed into sound and heat too as the car slows down.

Water-wheels (Sc4) Moving water possesses energy which can be harnessed to do a number of useful jobs. Efficient harnessing means as much water energy is changed into useful energy as possible. The design and positioning of the blades will affect the efficiency of the water-wheel.

Ice cold (Sc4) Heat can be thought of as a form of energy. It travels from hot areas to colder ones and can be slowed down by the use of insulation. This sheet simulates a simple investigation which the children might carry out themselves. Supply squared paper for them to draw a graph of their imaginary results.

Spirals and candles (Sc4) Hot air is less dense than the surrounding cooler air. If it is free to move, it will float upwards in the same way as a submerged piece of wood floats up in water. In this activity the children can explore the effect of using different-sized spirals. Take care with the naked flame. Do not allow the thread to burn. This model allows children to experience a series of changes of energy from fuel (in the candle wax) to heat and light (in the flame) to movement (of the spiral).

Energy from oil (Sc4) This short exercise might follow a discussion of how oil and other fossil fuels are formed under the Earth's crust. Discuss how the process of extracting and burning fossil fuels is irreversible. This often leads to the misconception that energy is used up. In fact, it is changed into less useful forms; heat and light.

Cooling a hot drink (Sc4) This is a simulation of an investigation where the children could represent the results in graphical form and then make some interpretations and a prediction.

Balloon rocket (Sc4) This investigation focuses on the energy stored in squeezed or stretched things. The energy changes are: stored 'springy' energy to movement to raised (potential) energy in the balloon. The children will need help in setting up the vertical string.

Make a mouse (Sc4) This is an easy vehicle to make because it does not rely on wheels and axles and the chassis is very simple. The rim of the plastic bottle top may need strengthening with some wire to prevent it being pulled in. Fix this on with sticky tape. Talk about the energy changes involved from the movement needed to wind the toy up to stored 'springy' energy in the elastic band to the final movement of the toy.

Electricity

DANGER – electricity! (Sc4) This picture contains most of the classic dangers associated with electricity in and around the home. It is important to discuss the issues once the task is completed.
❑ The children could make safety posters based on one or more of the features in the picture.

Lighting the bulb (Sc4) Children rarely look closely at the typical torch bulb to distinguish its separate parts which they must identify in order to use this sheet. These circuits will light the bulb: 2, 3, 4, 8, 11 and perhaps 10.

Making it flow (Sc3, 4) The children will find that most metals will conduct electricity if their surfaces are clean. A short length of pencil lead, however, will also conduct a current and the children may need help to understand that this is not a metal.

What can electricity do? (Sc4) This sheet will help children think about the effects of electricity. It is written so that the children will think of electricity as a form of energy which changes into another form. Some answers involve more than one change; for example, television – sound, light and magnetism.

Inventing diagrams (Sc4) This sheet leads children to appreciate the need for circuit diagrams by encouraging them to invent their own symbols for electrical components.
❑ The children could use their own symbols or the internationally-accepted ones to draw circuits for their friends to make.

Sending messages (Sc4) This activity enables children to experience the excitement of sending messages by Morse code. The wires should be as long as possible. The children will need some practice in sending and receiving Morse code, and should begin with single letters or words.

Electric motor (Sc4) The children will need to understand simple electric circuits to follow this activity. If the battery terminals or the motor terminals are reversed, then the motor will turn in the opposite direction. Two batteries will increase the speed and power of the motor, while the addition of a bulb will increase the resistance in the circuit and thus slow or stop the motor. Similarly, a pencil lead will increase the electrical resistance.

Making switches (Sc4) This sheet shows a simple, but effective, technique for making electrical components using plastic, card and aluminium foil.

Electromagnetism (Sc4) When a current is carried through a wire, a small magnetic field is produced which has a circular direction around the wire. This field can be detected when the wire is brought close to a magnetic compass. Here the children can investigate the effect of using more and more wire to produce this magnetic effect. This is measured by the degree of deflection given to the compass needle.

Clown's face (Sc4) This simple face can be made to light up in a variety of ways. Bulbs in bulb holders can be pushed through from the back and made to light up using a variety of switches. A buzzer could be added.

Wheel of fortune (Sc4) This simple model can be made with an electric motor. An arrow fitted to the motor is made to spin by flicking the current on and off. Secure the arrow to a small plastic pulley wheel fitted to the motor's spindle.

Pressure pad (Sc4) A simple pressure pad can be made using two semi-rigid plates of corrugated plastic or cardboard with strips of aluminium foil glued to them. The plates are separated by thin pads of card in the corners. Different sensitivities can be obtained by using different thicknesses of the card pads.

Car-park barrier (Sc4) The electromagnetic effect of a current can be used to move parts in a device. Electric bells and loudspeakers work on this principle. When a current is flowing through the coiled wire in the model, the iron nail will be pulled down towards it, thus lifting the barrier. Experiment with the relative positions of the nail and coil of wire.

Light and colour

Rainbow (Sc4) This sheet will enable children to focus on the colours of the spectrum as seen in a rainbow. It would complement an activity in which they made their own 'rainbow' with a mirror and a bowl of water or other means.

Making shadows (Sc4) The children will have to ignore the shadows from their fingers or else they may find it useful to fix the shapes they use on to a cocktail stick with a small piece of Blu-Tack.

Camouflaging fish (Sc1, 4) The children are free to camouflage the fish in any way they wish using both pattern and colour. The children can carry out a science investigation through this activity when they compare the camouflaged effect of the three types of patterned fish.

Camouflaged moths (Sc1, 4) In this activity, the children are investigating the effect of pattern only on how well the moth is camouflaged. The variable of colour (also present in 'Camouflaging fish', page 87) having been controlled.

Rainbow wheel (Sc4) This is a favourite activity for children to explore. Younger children may need help with spinning the wheel. This could, however, be placed in the chuck of a hand drill and then spun quite easily by the children.

Reflections (Sc4) This is an ingenious method for recording where the image in a mirror appears to be, since it is possible to see through the 'mirror' to the drawing as well as the reflection. It will enable children to understand that this image is the same distance behind the mirror as the object in front and that it is laterally inverted.

Spots before your eyes (Sc1, 4) This activity which explores one type of optical illusion. It leads on to a series of investigations which can be planned and carried out by the children themselves. The emphasis is on *finding out what happens if...*; rather than explaining why.

Bending light (Sc4) Lenses depend on light changing direction as it passes through them (refraction). This effect can be explored by looking at an object through a 'water lens' which the children can alter themselves.

Fun with mirrors (Sc1, 4) This activity explores the basis on which a kaleidoscope is made. Plane mirrors placed at an angle to each other will produce different numbers of reflections of an object placed in front. Number of images: 20°=17, 30°=11, 45°=7, 60°=5, 90°=3, 120°=2.

Tubular pin-hole camera (Sc1, 4) One of the problems with a pin-hole camera is that light falls on the screen from the viewer's side as well as from inside the camera. This simple design overcomes this problem to give a clearer image.
❑ The children can experiment with different-sized holes, replacing the foil when necessary.

Sound

Sound makers (Sc4) The children should gain experience of making sounds themselves before making the classifications suggested on this sheet. Their attention should be focused on the part of the instrument making the sound and, therefore, the part which is vibrating.

Which is loudest? (Sc4) Placing sounds in order of loudness will start children thinking about measuring the volume of sounds.
❑ The children might like to number the sounds on their chart and use this scale to 'measure' other sounds against. For instance, the loudness of a piano may fall between a television and a guitar and be awarded 5½ on the scale.

Mystery sounds (Sc4) The children will need to set up a screen or, alternatively, they could have their collection of 'sounds' in a box. If they are given some time to investigate unusual sounds first, this will be of benefit to the final sound quiz.
❑ Encourage partners to describe the sounds they hear by using words such as 'scraping', 'clanging', 'soft', 'high-pitched' and so on or by comparing the sound with another more familiar or common sound, 'It sounds like a waterfall'.

Sound survey (Sc4) Children (and adults) are always surprised by the number of sounds around us which we take for granted. By closing our eyes and listening hard we can pick up a wide variety of sounds in different locations.

What makes sounds? (Sc4) Children easily use words such as *vibrations* before they have formed a clear idea of what these are. This sheet will help them consolidate their ideas about vibrations by looking, feeling and listening carefully. Encourage them to record what they can see and feel when sounds are made.
❑ A similar experience with musical instruments will reinforce the concept of vibration.

Making sounds louder (Sc1, 4) The children may know that an electric amplifier makes sounds louder on a hi-fi system. This activity helps them to understand that sounds can be amplified in other ways. Instruments such as a guitar and a drum have sound boxes to amplify their sounds. This model simulates the old-style gramophone, which amplified the vibrations in its needle by using a large horn.

High and low sounds (Sc4) At the end of this activity, the children should understand that we get higher pitched sounds when smaller things vibrate. For instance, the shorter the length of elastic band or the smaller the amount of air in the bottle the higher the pitch of the note produced.

Materials

Collections (Sc3) The children will need guidance in choosing a particular material each time they use this sheet. They should try to describe the characteristics of the material rather than individual objects made from it. You might like to add other descriptive words to the sheet which are appropriate to the chosen material.

In the kitchen (Sc3) This sheet will focus the children's attention on the variety of materials used to make the objects found in the kitchen. Discuss why a particular material has been used for a particular object.

In the classroom (Sc3) Again attention is focused on the materials used to make objects. ❏ The children could make a collection of classroom objects made from a certain material.

Making with materials (Sc3) This activity gives a further opportunity to think about raw materials. Different children may choose to join the objects to different materials depending on their experience; for example, the boat could be made from wood or plastic. Many things are made from more than one material – to which material or materials should they be joined? Can the children find some of these and draw them on to their sheets?

Comparing materials: 1 (Sc3) Exploring the properties of materials is done most easily by using properties which are opposites. Each of the materials at the top of the page should be drawn once in each of the tables. For instance: bendy – cotton, card, tissue, polythene; stiff – wood, metal. Discuss how the amount of a material present may affect its properties; for instance, a thin strip of metal could be bendy, but a metal girder is stiff.

Comparing materials: 2 (Sc3) This is similar to the previous sheet (page 106), but includes different properties.

Cartoons of properties (Sc3) Drawing cartoons is one way of focusing on the properties of materials by exaggerating them. For example, given the property 'elastic', a child might choose and illustrate a bungee jump or a bouncing ball.

The wrong substance (Sc3) What is it about stainless steel that makes it suitable for making cutlery? This sheet asks similar questions in an indirect way. Encourage the children to discuss why the material illustrated is inappropriate and why the usual material is best.

Runny liquids (Sc1, 3) This activity looks at one property of liquids – viscosity or runniness. A simple test is suggested, but the details will have to be worked out by the children. The slope could be a sheet of card, but the best angle of slope will have to be found by trial and error.

Earth in space

Star constellations (Sc4) This sheet introduces constellations as imaginary pictures in the sky. While the children may find it difficult to spot the real constellations, they can begin to recognise the patterns by drawing their own pictures.

Seasonal shadows (Sc4) This sheet explores a number of ideas. First, that shadows move and change length during the day and second, that shadows are different in summer and winter. Discuss: how shadows move from west to east due to the rotation of the Earth, shortening as the Sun rises in the sky towards midday; how the Sun appears to move from east to west; and that in winter the Sun does not rise as high in the sky as in summer. *Answers* (clockwise from top right): summer – 3 pm, 8 am, 10 am, 6 am, 12 am, 11 am; winter – 9 am, 11 am, 10 am, 2 pm, 1 pm, 12 am.

How big is everything? (Sc4) This sheet looks at the relative sizes of the Universe, our galaxy, our solar system and our planet. All of these are difficult concepts for young children.

The inner solar system (Sc4) This simple model will help children to understand how the Sun and the three nearest planets relate to each other. The model can show how the moon orbits the Earth, how the planets orbit the Sun and how eclipses are formed. It does *not* show relative sizes, positions and distances. One day passing is achieved by rotating the Earth once, one month by rotating the moon disc once, a full moon by placing it on the opposite side of the Earth to the Sun and a new moon by placing it on the same side as the Sun. One year passes when the Earth and moon goes once round the Sun (rotate the whole model). The moon would orbit 12 times round the Earth while doing this.

Our solar system (Sc4) This introduces children to all the planets in our solar system. From the Sun, they should be arranged: Mercury, Venus, Earth, Mars, Jupiter, Saturn, Uranus, Neptune, Pluto. To compare the relative sizes of the planets, the children will need to understand radius and how to use a pair of compasses.

Solids and shadows (Sc4) This activity helps children to understand how a single source of light illuminates only part of an object leaving the rest in shadow. This knowledge is necessary for their understanding of phases of the moon.

Mysteries in the dark (Sc4) This sheet provides further help in understanding light and shadows.

Moon models (Sc4) Children are not always able to observe the moon at first hand over a period of a month. This simulation will help them to make sense of what they see when they do get the chance. There are two ways of 'looking' at the solar system: from outside looking down or from the surface of the Earth itself. By using the child's head to represent the Earth, he or she will get the familiar view from the Earth itself. A darkened room and/or a strong light are important for this demonstration. *Answers*: 1=g, 2=a, 3=e, 4=d, 5=h, 6=f, 7=b, 8=c.

Spinning on its axis (Sc4) To understand the effect of the tilt of the Earth's axis the children need to 'step into space' and look back. This is helped by introducing two imaginary planets with extreme axis tilts. Edith will experience a long day while Edward's day will be short. Vera and Vernon will have days and nights of equal duration. Hannah will have constant daylight and will see the sun going round in circles in the sky, while Harry remains in darkness.

❏ The children may be able to draw and predict what would happen on these three planets six months later when we can assume they are on the other side of the Sun but their axes are still pointing the same way.

Space and time (Sc4) Many of our periods of time are governed by the relative movements of the planets and moon. There is a distinction made on the sheet between pictures that show the passage of time (in each case an arrow shows the corresponding movement) and those which show a particular period in time. The Earth spins round once in *one day* and half way round

in *12 hours*. The moon goes round the Earth in *one month* and a quarter of the way round in *one week*. The Earth goes once round the Sun in *one year*. When the northern hemisphere is tilted towards the Sun it is *summer in Britain* and when tilted away from the Sun it is *winter in Britain*.

Time and change

Weather pictures (Sc1) This activity introduces children to the use of symbols to record the weather over a week. They may not need all the symbols or they may need to make some more of their own.

Disappearing puddles (Sc3) This activity helps children to observe the effect of evaporation both inside and outside the classroom. Make the puddles on a sunny day when the evaporation will be greatest. In the classroom the saucer can be placed near, say, a radiator and compared with one elsewhere, away from a heat source.

How much time? (Sc1, 4) This sheet gives children practice in the skill of using a timer as well as predicting how long something will take.

Time of day (Sc4) Being able to see the day at a glance can be quite revealing for children. What proportion of the day do they spend eating or doing school work? They will have to write in note form into the space provided or the sheet could be photocopied to A3 size.

❏ Could the children fill in a similar sheet for their weekends? How do these days differ?

Weather forecasts (Sc1) This exercise compares a prediction with reality. The weather forecasts can be found from a variety of sources: a newspaper is the easiest to use, but the Met. Office will supply forecasts by fax or telephone. Cloud cover may not be included in a forecast, but can be estimated by the children on the day.

Rainfall (Sc3) This activity will give practice in recording and displaying results, as well as reading capacity in millilitres. This sheet could precede or follow a similar real exercise carried out in school.

Sundial (Sc4) This exercise simulates the effect of a sundial. It would be a useful preliminary exercise to the children making their own sundial outside.

Cycles model This cut-out model should be used with the following four pages (129–132) about cycles of various kinds. It folds up to form a spiral, which suggests that a cycle does not return to its beginning but progresses onwards while following the same patterns. The smaller sectors are for the text supplied with some of the cycles, indicating the time periods involved.

Cycles: people (Sc2) This demonstrates the human life cycle and provides an approximate time span between each stage. This work should be supported by further reference work as well as discussions.

Cycles: housefly (Sc2) This life cycle is an example of one in which the adult is quite different in appearance to the young. The eggs hatch a few hours after being laid and another five days pass before the larva turns into pupa. The pupa hatches in three days into an adult fly which can reproduce within 14 days.

Cycles: buttercup plant (Sc2) It is possible to begin anywhere in the life cycle of a flowering plant, but the seed in the soil would seem an obvious starting point.

❏ Compare one part of the life cycle in different plants. For instance, compare different seeds from different plants or how each is pollinated.

Cycles: the water cycle (Sc3) This is not a living cycle but, nevertheless, one which is continually repeated. The children should gain experience of some of the major features of the water cycle before representing it formally as a diagram or model. The concepts of evaporation, condensation and filtration could be explored practically first.

Flying models

Glider (Sc1, 4) This model is best launched by holding the tail between forefinger and thumb and pushing gently away on a slightly downward path.
❏ What happens if two paper clips are used? What happens if the wings are folded more closely together? What happens if you make a similar model twice or three times the size? Can the children make the plane curve round to the left or to the right? Try cutting part of the tail off – what happens?

Spinners (Sc1, 4) Spinners are very useful for giving experience in controlling variables. The two spinners shown are identical apart from the shape/area of the wings. Any difference in their performances can be attributed to this one variable. It would be too difficult to time the drop of each spinner with sufficient accuracy so the best method for comparing them is to release them both together and see which lands first. Explore the effects of adding another paper clip, making larger wings or using a different material to make the spinner.

Tube glider (Sc1, 4) Gliders do not need to have conventional wings in order to glide. This model is best launched in a similar way to the glider on page 133, by holding the point of the tube and pushing it away gently. Again, the children could investigate the effect of changing one feature (variable) at a time, such as the length or diameter of the tube or the material from which it is made.

Parachute (Sc1, 4) A parachute drops slowly because it encounters air resistance under its canopy. If this trapped air cannot escape as it falls, the canopy will become unstable, possibly turning over. The hole in the middle of the canopy should release this air. If the hole is too large too much air will escape. Let the children investigate the effect of making different-sized holes in the canopy.
❏ What happens if the canopy is made larger?

Winged seed model (Sc1, 2, 4) This model is based on the winged seed of a sycamore tree. It is much larger than the real seed, but it will spin if dropped in the correct way. It flies best when started on its side. Let the children experiment with different ways of dropping the models.
❏ Can the children make a similar model but twice the size? Will it still spin?

Measuring skills

Circumferences (Sc1) This activity gives children practice in measuring circumferences using either string or a strip of paper. They should make a guess before measuring each circumference. Each subsequent guess will be informed by the ones made before, so there should be an improvement in their predictions.

Match the volume (Sc1) This sheet aims to build up the concept of volume in relation to everyday containers. It might follow considerable practice in measuring capacity. *Answers*: teaspoon 5ml, tablespoon 8ml, saucer 40ml, egg cup 40ml, film canister 30ml, teacup 150ml, kitchen mug 300ml, tin can 500ml, pint milk bottle 550ml, 10cm cube 1000ml.

Matching mass (Sc1) This is similar to the 'Match the volume' sheet (page 139). It is best done by ordering the objects first then matching these against the given masses. The children will learn

most when they check these approximate values. *Answers:* fork 60g, baked beans 420g, empty milk bottle 225g, large 1.5v torch battery 100g, ten marbles 50g, 50 lolly sticks 28g, milk bottle full of water 775g.

Match the temperature (Sc1, 3) Children should not measure the temperature of boiling water or hot tap water unless supervised. The temperatures illustrated may vary. For example, the hot tap water and the outside temperature will depend on local conditions.
Answers: crushed ice cubes 0°C, refrigerator 5–10°C, outside 8°C, cold tap water 8°C, inside 20°C, palm of hand 30°C, arm pit 32°C, hot tap water 40°C, boiling water 100°C.

Shade detective (Sc4) This sheet enables children to measure the shade or tone of a colour. An arbitrary scale is provided against which children can match shades or colours from newspapers and magazines. Ordering the samples should precede the actual measuring.

Measuring area (Sc1, 2) This is a standard way of estimating the area of an irregular shape such as a leaf. The children could adopt the rule that if more than half the square is inside the shape then count it, otherwise don't.

Wheat seedlings (Sc1, 2) This sheet encourages children to take their measurements, represent them graphically and then look for patterns in their results. The simple pattern which will emerge is a normal distribution curve with a high number of 'average' seedlings and a few which are small or large. This pattern is one which the children will find repeated in similar exercises involving growing things.
❏ Measure the heights of the children in the class and plot the results in a similar way. Many other measurements, such as handspan, shoe size and so on, will give similar results.

Primary topic grid

Topics	Pages
Air	16, 17, 26, 27, 28, 52, 67, 99, 121, 132–137, 141
Animals	29–39, 51, 87, 88, 130
Change	16, 24, 25, 27, 48, 66, 68, 69, 89, 91, 112, 119–132
Clothes	21, 22, 24, 25, 87, 88
Colour and light	15, 73, 81, 85–94, 111, 112, 116–119, 127, 142
Communications	16, 17, 18, 77, 94, 95, 121
Earth and space	68, 70, 85, 86, 111–121, 127
Electricity	72–84
Energy	27, 62–84, 141
Environment	16, 29–45, 48, 49, 62, 68, 87, 88, 98, 121, 130, 131, 132, 141, 143
Flight	33, 34, 70, 133–137
Food	16, 20, 22, 23, 38, 42, 43, 44, 46, 47, 66, 69, 139
Forces	50–61, 70, 84, 110, 136
Growth	20–25, 40, 41, 45, 46, 48, 49, 51, 129, 130, 131, 144
Homes	36, 37, 39, 72, 75, 87, 88, 103, 139
Hot and cold	66, 67, 69, 121, 141
Journeys	52, 61, 64, 111, 133–136
Magnets	55, 80
Materials	56–60, 66, 74, 79, 83, 102–110
Metals	74, 79, 102, 105
Minibeasts	29–32, 35–38, 88, 130
Moving things	21, 27, 29–34, 50–53, 55, 60, 61, 63, 64, 65, 67, 70, 71, 78, 82, 84, 87, 95, 99, 110, 133–137
Ourselves	15–28, 50, 51, 62, 72, 91, 97, 99, 123, 124, 129, 138, 144
Ponds	32, 39, 65, 87, 122
School	29, 30, 32–35, 37, 83, 104, 121, 124, 126
Shops	16, 43, 44, 46, 47, 84
Sound	17, 33, 34, 77, 95–101
Healthy living	15–28, 51, 62, 72, 124, 129, 144
Time and seasons	27, 29–34, 111, 112, 118–132
Toys and games	21, 51, 52, 59, 63–67, 70, 71, 81, 82, 84, 93, 94, 133–137
Transport	51, 52, 53, 58, 60, 61,70, 78, 84, 133–137
Water	31, 32, 58, 65, 87, 92, 110, 122, 132
Weather	67, 85, 119, 121, 122, 125, 126, 127, 132, 141

Name _____

Looking at eyes

You will need: a small mirror.

♣ Use the mirror to look at one of your eyes.

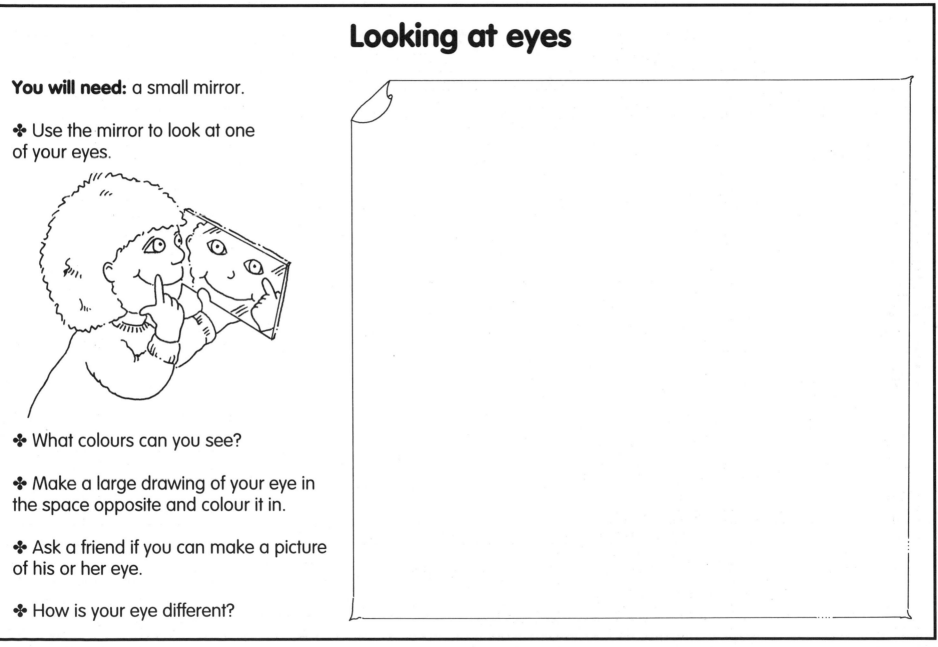

♣ What colours can you see?

♣ Make a large drawing of your eye in the space opposite and colour it in.

♣ Ask a friend if you can make a picture of his or her eye.

♣ How is your eye different?

The sense of smell

The sense of smell

✤ Make up a test to find out if your friends can tell which smell is which.

You will need: six small containers, six smelly things.

✤ You may like to consider these questions:
• Will you cover your containers?
• Will you blindfold your friends?
• Will you label your containers?
• How will you record your results?

✤ Record your results on the table below. You may like also to write in which smell is which letter.

Name	Smell (Tick if guessed correctly.)					
	A	B	C	D	E	F

Big ears

✤ Try this hearing test with a friend.

• Drop numbered cards closer and closer to your friend until he or she hears one.
• Record the number of the first card that is heard.

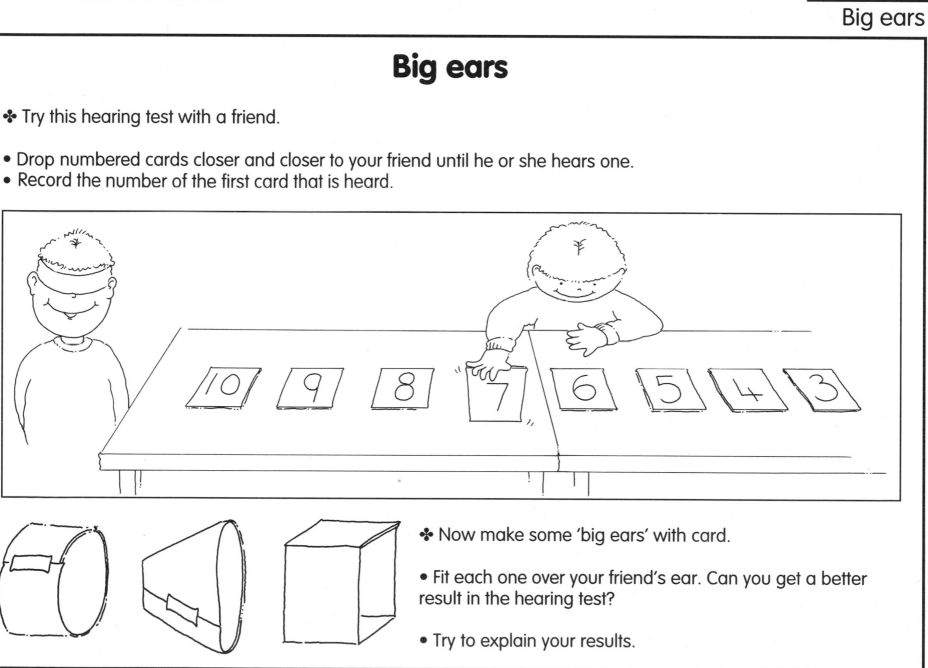

✤ Now make some 'big ears' with card.

• Fit each one over your friend's ear. Can you get a better result in the hearing test?

• Try to explain your results.

Touch test

⚠️ Take care!

How sensitive is your friend's touch?
Is each finger the same?

♣ Use the touch test below to find out.

You will need: a thick pad
of newspapers, a drawing pin.

- Put this sheet on a thick pad of newspapers.
- Use a drawing pin to push a hole through each dot in the strip above.
- Turn the page over.
- Ask a friend to feel each dot pattern and tell you how many dots there are.
- Record your results on another piece of paper and then copy them into the table opposite.

Name	Score out of 5		
	Forefinger	**Little finger**	**Thumb**

Fingerprints

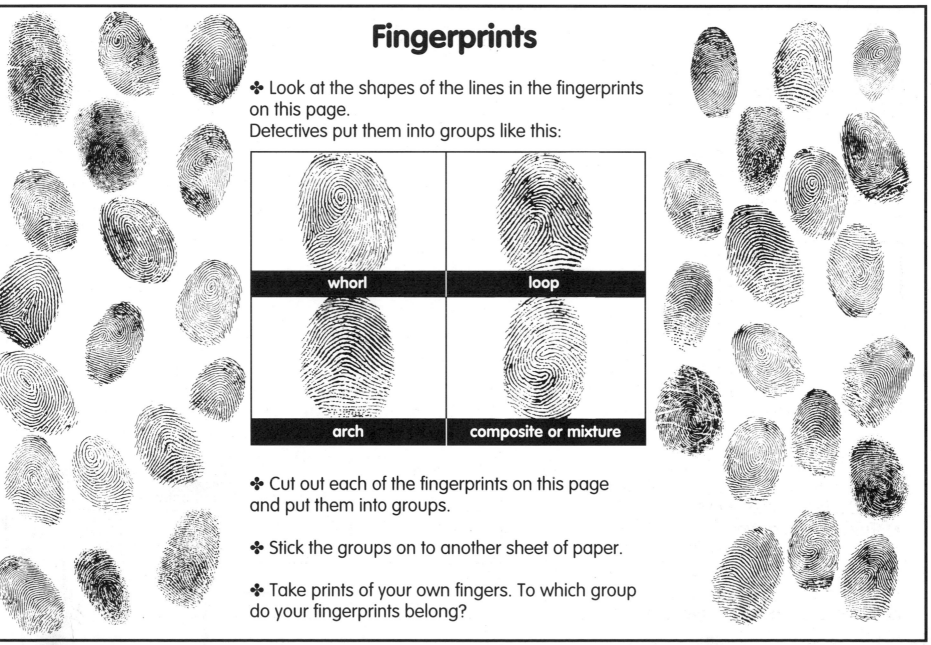

❖ Look at the shapes of the lines in the fingerprints on this page.
Detectives put them into groups like this:

whorl	loop
arch	composite or mixture

❖ Cut out each of the fingerprints on this page and put them into groups.

❖ Stick the groups on to another sheet of paper.

❖ Take prints of your own fingers. To which group do your fingerprints belong?

False teeth

False teeth

You will need: two paper fasteners, cotton thread, a small mirror.

♣ Cut out the shapes below to make a model of healthy teeth.

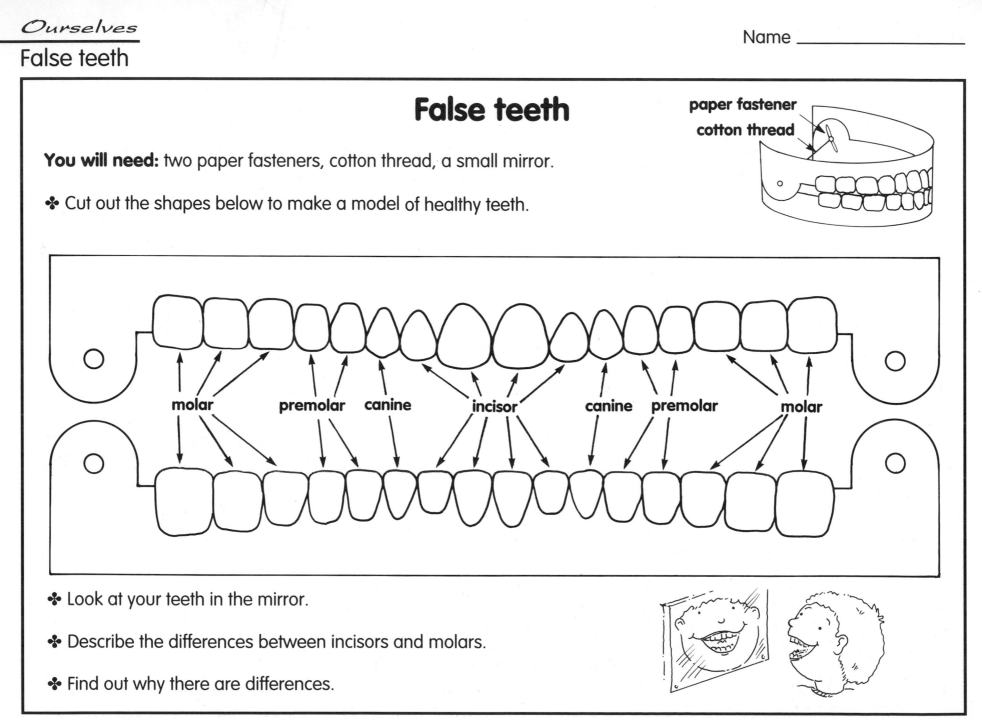

♣ Look at your teeth in the mirror.

♣ Describe the differences between incisors and molars.

♣ Find out why there are differences.

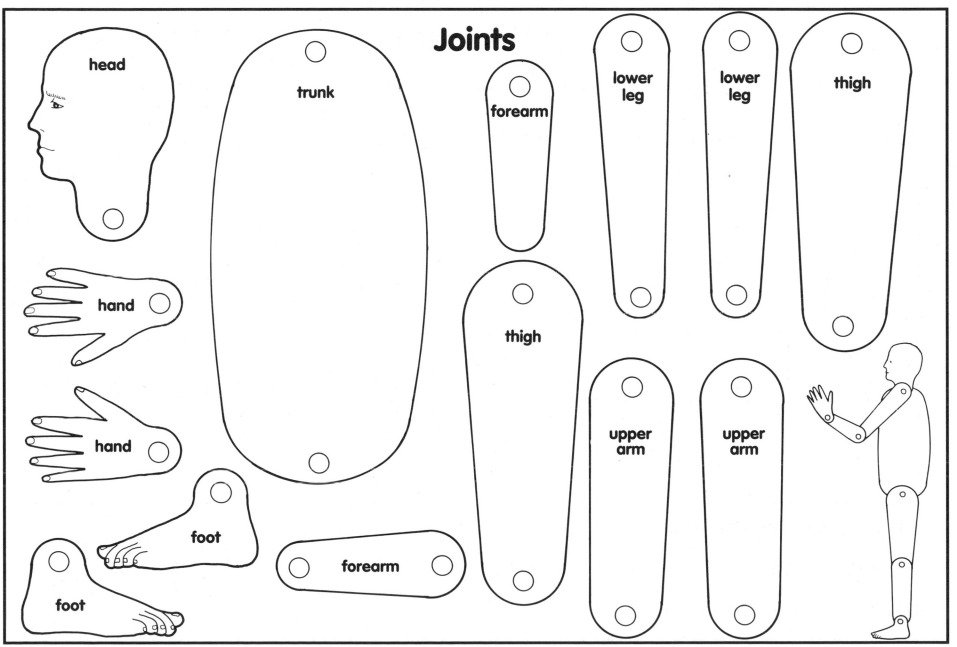

Joints

head

trunk

forearm

lower leg

lower leg

thigh

hand

thigh

hand

foot

forearm

upper arm

upper arm

foot

The body

The body

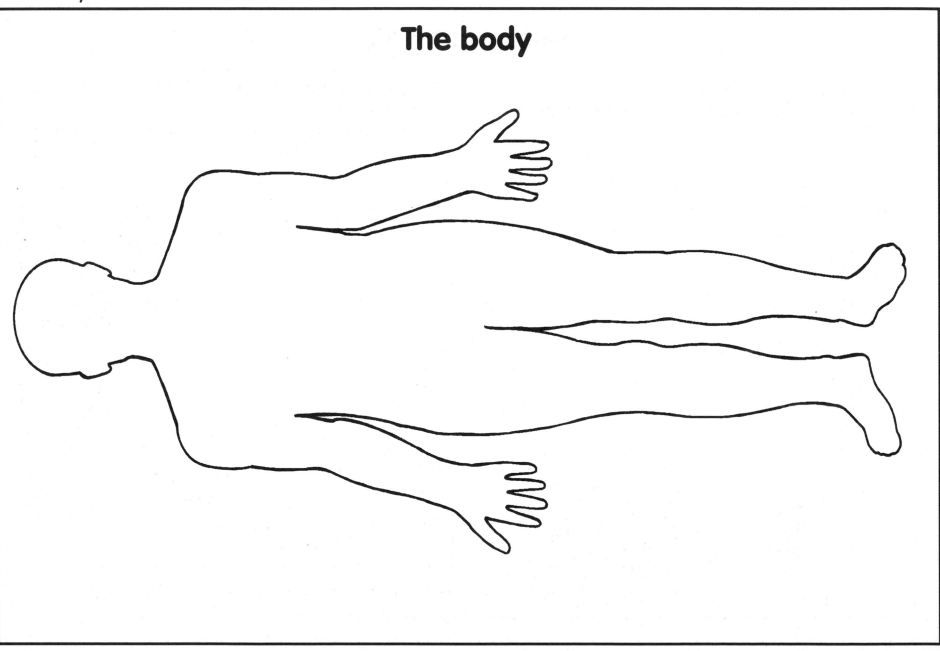

Name _____

Inside our bodies

These are some of the bones that support our bodies.
✤ Cut them out and stick all the bones except the ribs on to the body outline.

These are some of the things (organs) which we have inside our bodies.
✤ Cut them out and stick them on to the body outline.

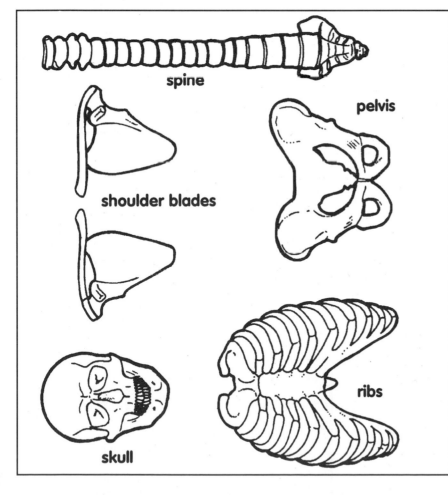

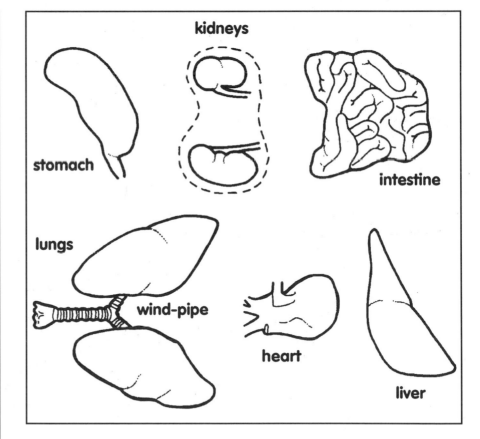

✤ Finally, stick on some ribs over the heart and lungs to protect them.

Name _____

Measuring people: 1

Measuring people: 1

You will need: a measuring tape, a metre ruler, a small ruler.

❖ Measure parts of your body and complete the table below. Each time choose the best measuring instrument.

❖ Do the same for some friends.

Parts of the body \ Names	Me					
Length of foot (cm)						
Handspan (cm)						
Circumference of head (cm)						
Circumference of waist (cm)						
Circumference of wrist (cm)						
Height (cm)						
Distance between outstretched arms (cm)						
Distance between eyes (cm)						

Measuring people: 2

Does the tallest person in your survey have the biggest head?

♣ Complete this scattergraph using the information in the table on sheet 1.

♣ Write about the pattern of the dots or the shape they make on your scattergraph.

♣ Think of some more investigations like this to make.

This person is 105cm tall with a head circumference of 40cm.

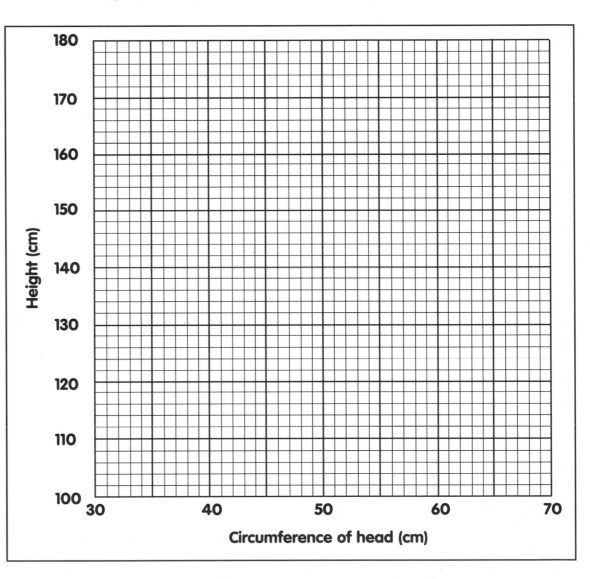

Name _____

How big are your lungs?

How big are your lungs?

Take care!

When you take a deep breath you fill your lungs with air.

❖ How much air does it take to fill your lungs? Do this experiment to find out.

You will need: some plastic tubing, a small polythene bag.

- Hold the bag tightly over the end of the tube.

- Take a deep breath.

- Fill the bag with air as many times as you can with one breath.

❖ How big are your lungs compared with a friend's lungs?

My lung capacity is ⬜ bags.

My friend's lung capacity is ⬜ bags.

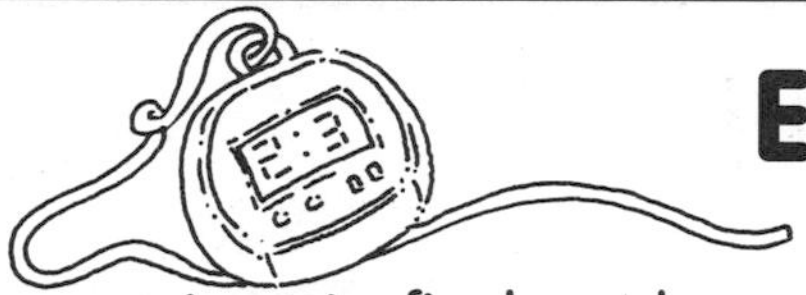

Exercise and breathing

♣ Work with a partner to find out how exercise affects your breathing.

You will need: a stop-watch.

• Count how many breaths your partner takes in one minute while resting. If you cannot see the breaths, ask your partner to place one hand on his/her chest while breathing in and out.

• Now ask your partner to do some strenuous exercise for a while. He or she could do **one** of the exercises shown opposite.

• Measure your partner's breathing rate again as soon as he or she finishes exercising. Make your measurements every minute for ten minutes and complete the table at the bottom of the sheet.

♣ How many minutes passed before your partner was breathing normally again?

♣ Try this experiment with different people and different exercises.

step-ups

press-ups

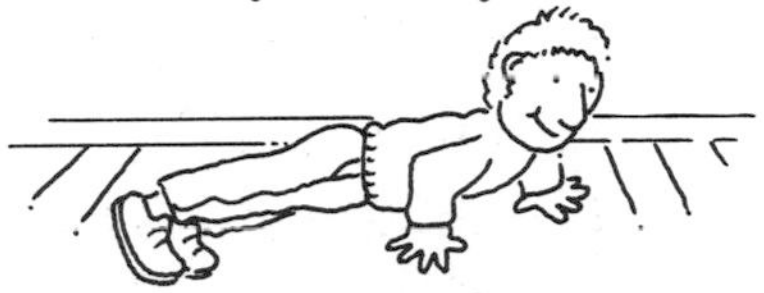

run around playground

standing broad jumps

	Before exercise	Minutes after exercise									
		1	2	3	4	5	6	7	8	9	10
Number of breaths every minute											

Name _____

Measuring lung capacity

You will need: a large plastic bottle, a length of plastic tubing, a bowl of water or access to a sink.

❖ Fill the bottle and a bowl or sink with water and hold it like this:

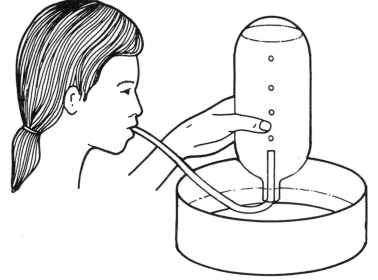

❖ Take a deep breath and blow out down the tube into the bottle.

❖ If you fill the bottle with air, hold your breath while it is filled with water again – then keep blowing.

❖ Compare your lung capacity with that of others in your class.

❖ Do the tallest people have the largest lungs?

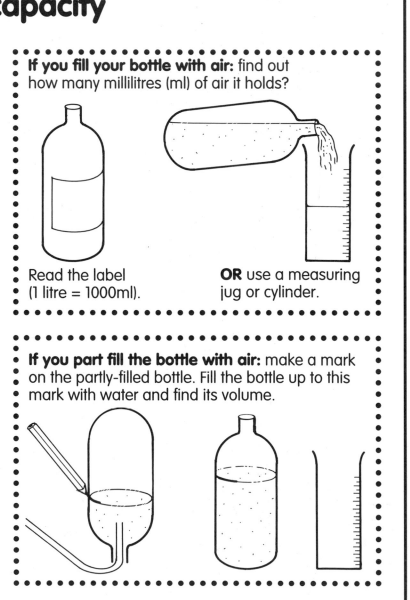

If you fill your bottle with air: find out how many millilitres (ml) of air it holds?

Read the label
(1 litre = 1000ml).

OR use a measuring jug or cylinder.

If you part fill the bottle with air: make a mark on the partly-filled bottle. Fill the bottle up to this mark with water and find its volume.

Name _____

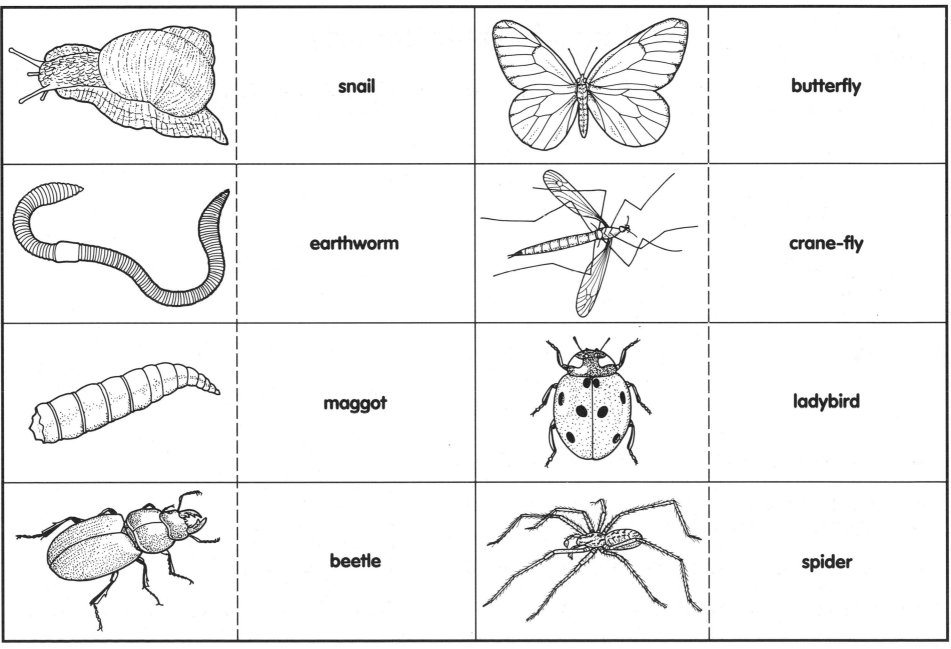

	snail		butterfly
	earthworm		crane-fly
	maggot		ladybird
	beetle		spider

Minibeasts: 2

Name _____

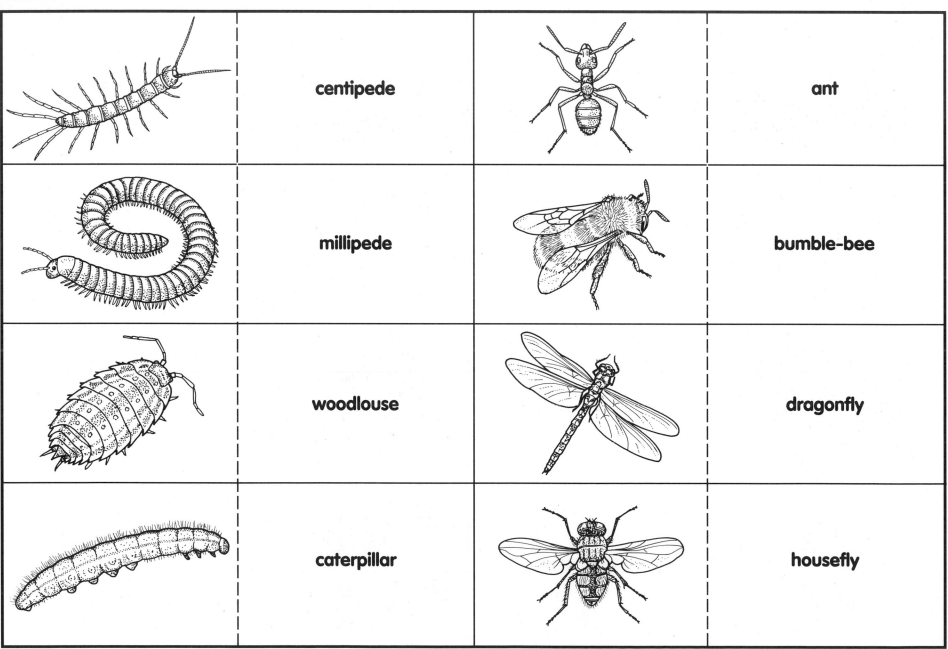

	centipede		ant
	millipede		bumble-bee
	woodlouse		dragonfly
	caterpillar		housefly

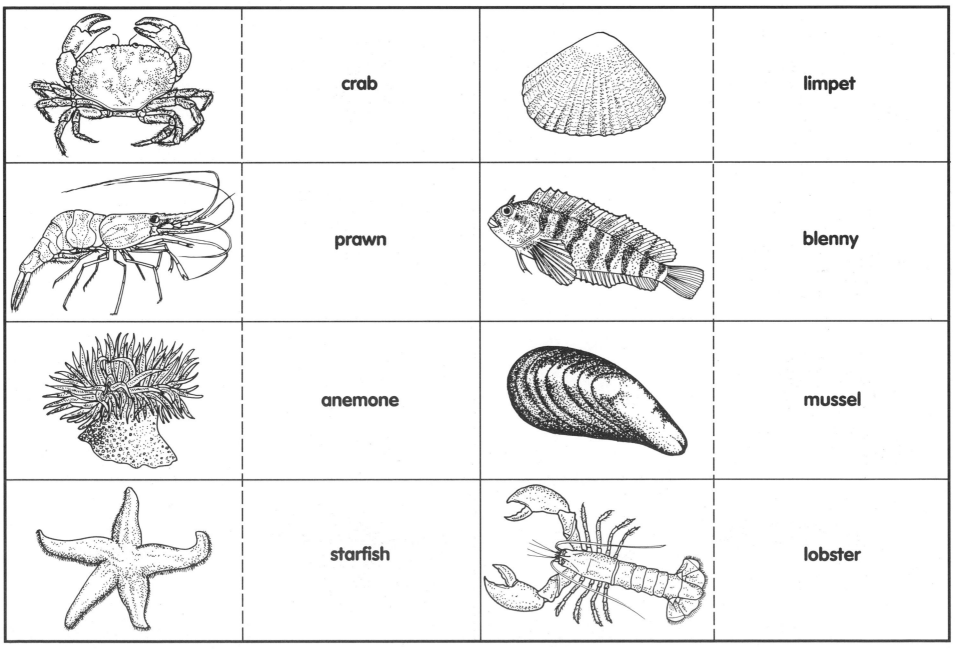

	crab		limpet
	prawn		blenny
	anemone		mussel
	starfish		lobster

Freshwater creatures

Name _____

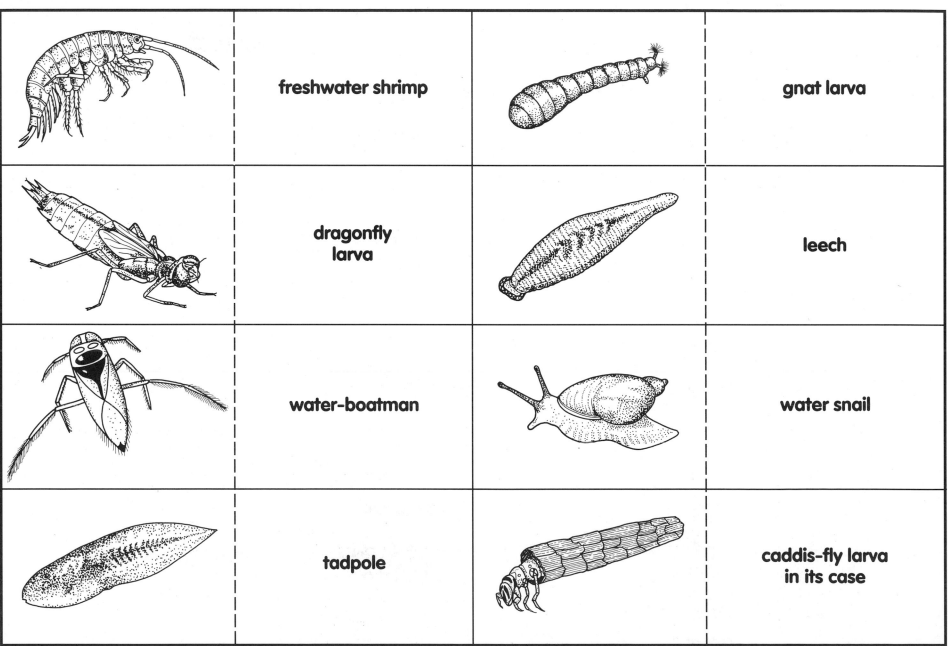

	freshwater shrimp		**gnat larva**
	dragonfly larva		**leech**
	water-boatman		**water snail**
	tadpole		**caddis-fly larva in its case**

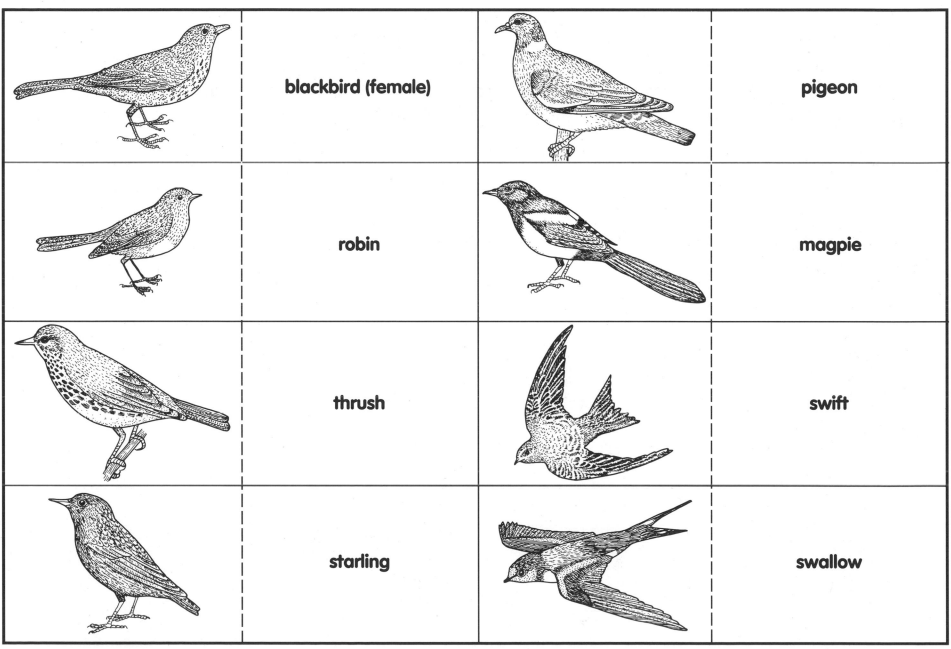

	blackbird (female)		pigeon
	robin		magpie
	thrush		swift
	starling		swallow

Birds: 2

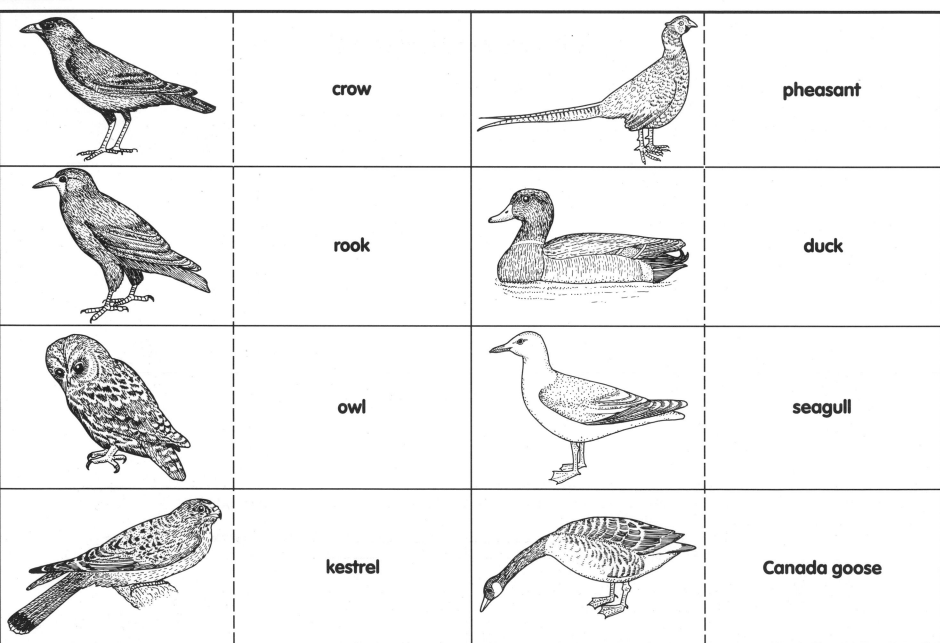

	crow	pheasant
	rook	duck
	owl	seagull
	kestrel	Canada goose

Identifying minibeasts

✤ Choose one of these minibeasts (a–k) and use this key to find out its name.

1 Minibeast has its wings showing. ——————— Go to 2
Minibeast has no wings showing. ——————— Go to 5

2 There is a single pair of wings. ——————— **housefly**
There are two pairs of wings. ——————— Go to 3

3 Minibeast has a long, thin abdomen. ——————— **damselfly**
Abdomen is not long and thin. ——————— Go to 4

4 Abdomen has different coloured stripes. ——————— **bumble-bee**
Abdomen is all the same colour. ——————— **honey-bee**

5 Minibeast has legs. ——————— Go to 7
Minibeast has no legs. ——————— Go to 6

6 Minibeast has tentacles. ——————— **slug**
Minibeast has no tentacles. ——————— **earthworm**

7 There are more than eight legs. ——————— Go to 8
There are eight legs or less. ——————— Go to 9

8 There is one pair of legs on each body segment. ——— **centipede**
There are two pairs of legs on each body segment. ——— **millipede**

9 There are eight legs. ——————— **harvestman**
There are six legs. ——————— Go to 10

10 Minibeast has 'antlers' on its head. ——————— **stag beetle**
Minibeast has no 'antlers'. ——————— **ant**

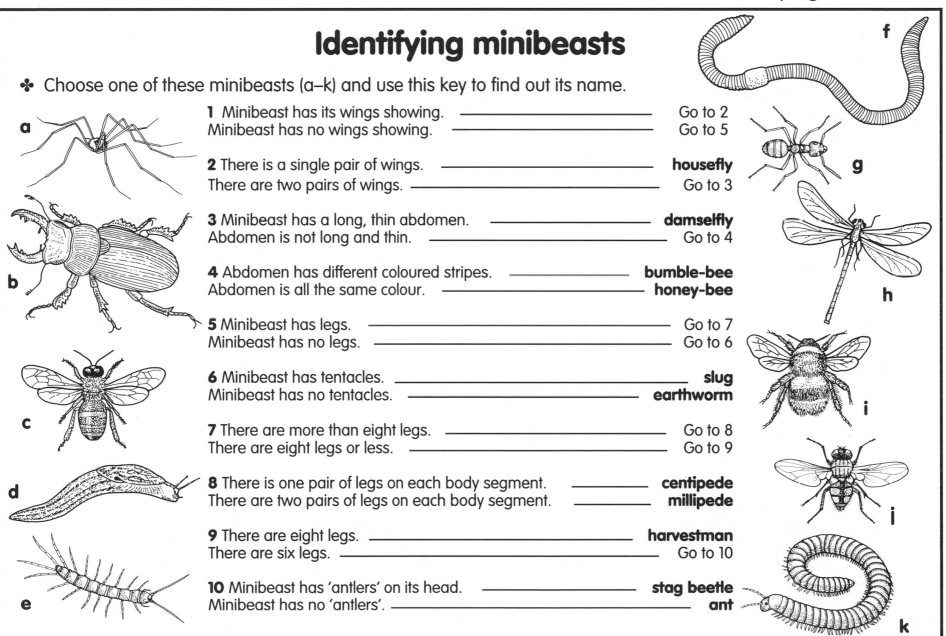

Minibeast habitats

Minibeast habitats

❖ Look at these groups of minibeasts and the places where they live.
❖ In each group, join the minibeast to its most likely habitat.

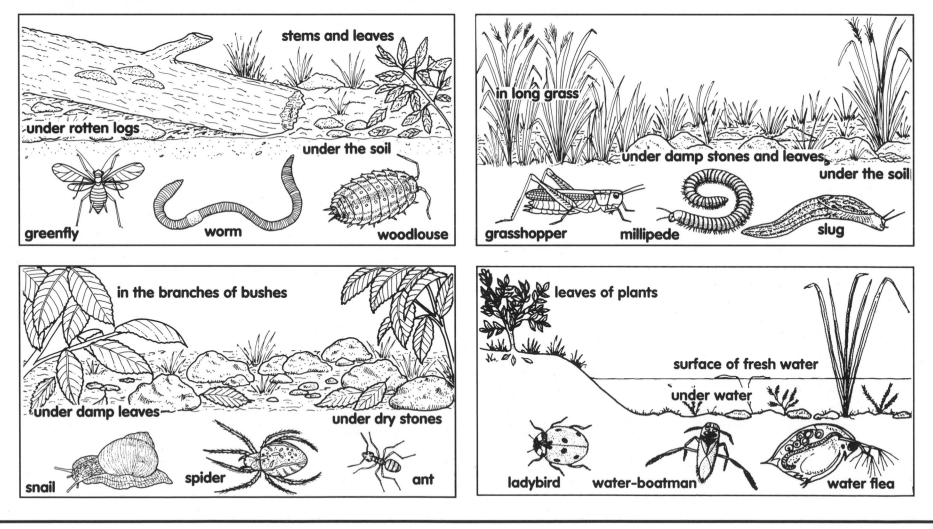

stems and leaves

under rotten logs

under the soil

greenfly   **worm**   **woodlouse**

in long grass

under damp stones and leaves

under the soil

grasshopper   **millipede**   **slug**

in the branches of bushes

under damp leaves

under dry stones

snail   **spider**   **ant**

leaves of plants

surface of fresh water

under water

ladybird   **water-boatman**   **water flea**

Describing habitats

The areas where animals and plants live are called **habitats**.
A habitat is just the right place for a particular living thing.

♣ Describe some habitats by filling in the table below.

Features / Habitats	dark	shady	light	wet	damp	dry	Is protection given from the weather?	Is food available there?	Is there protection from predators?
under stones									
under the soil									
in a rotting log									
on leaves of a plant									
among long grass									
in a stream									
in a pond									
in rotting leaves									
in garden compost									
on marsh land									

Food chains

Food chains

Here is a simple food chain:

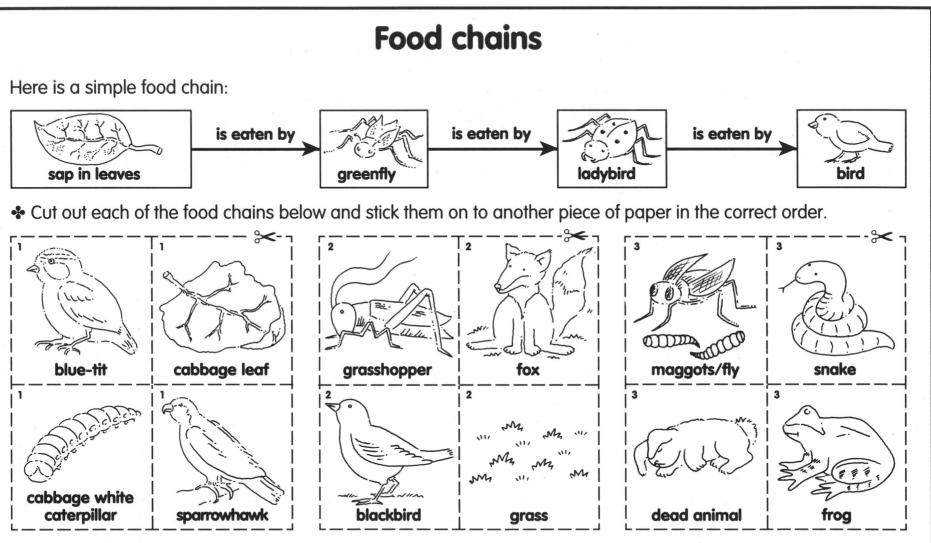

♣ Cut out each of the food chains below and stick them on to another piece of paper in the correct order.

♣ Now answer these questions:
• In chain **1**, what might happen if a lot of slugs were poisoned?
• In chain **2**, what might happen if the grasshoppers could not breed?
• In chain **3**, what might happen if there were too many frogs in an area?

The Daily Croaker

35p   **Issue 9999**

FROG POPULATION DECLINES

1 The old folk remember seeing lots of frogs around the village pond.

2 Two years ago a builder decided to build houses around the pond.

a The frog population has begun to grow and grow again.

b The villagers soon noticed the frog population becoming smaller.

c The builder filled in the pond.

d They could not lay eggs.

e Frogs always return to the pond in which they were born to lay new eggs (spawn).

f Later that year they found new spawn in the pond.

g Mr and Mrs Jenkins moved into one of the new houses and built a small pond in their garden.

h Last year the frogs found their pond was gone.

♣ Most of the sentences in this newspaper story are jumbled up. Number them in the correct order to tell the story. The first two have been sorted out for you.

♣ Draw a picture to go with the story.

Parts of a buttercup

Parts of a buttercup

♣ Label the parts of this buttercup using the words in the box at the bottom of the page.

♣ Write a sentence about each part describing what it does.

_____

_____

_____

_____

_____

_____

_____

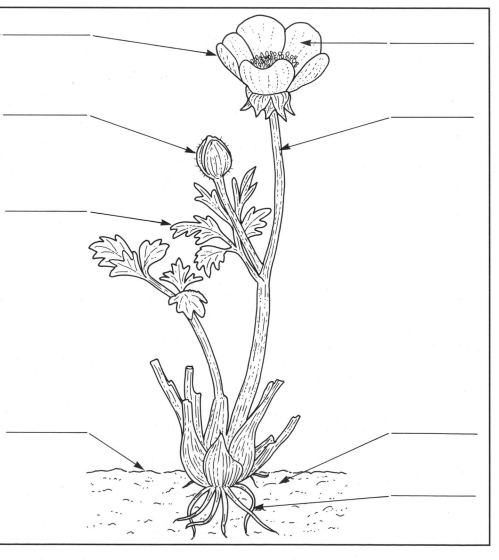

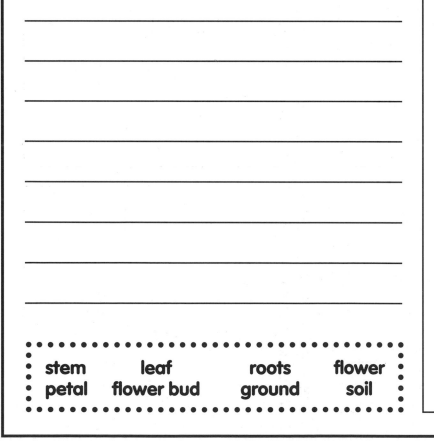

stem	leaf	roots	flower
petal	flower bud	ground	soil

Teacher Timesavers: Science

Name _____

Parts of plants

❖ Look at these pictures of different plants.
❖ Colour in the parts of the plants using the key opposite.

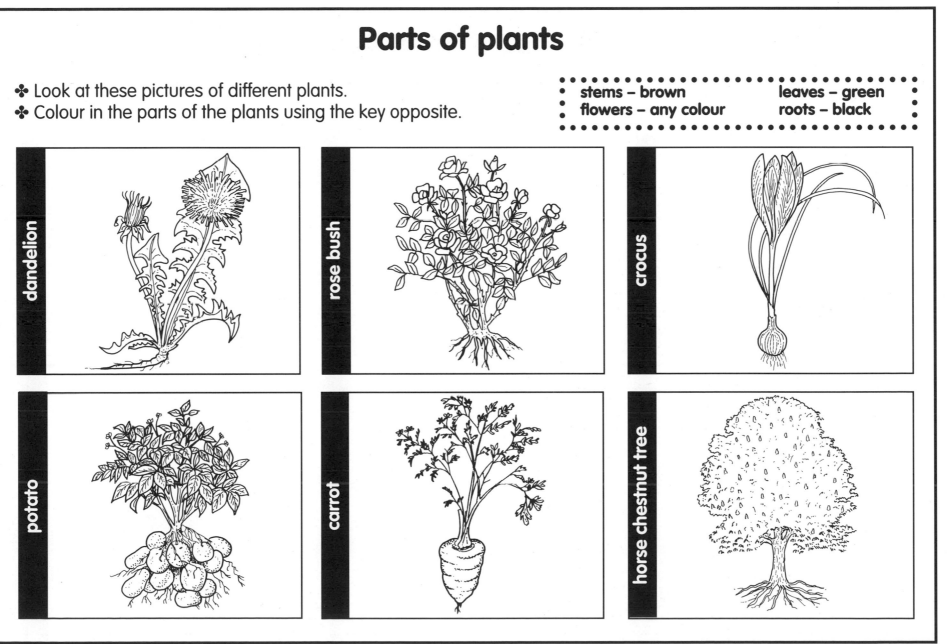

dandelion | rose bush | crocus

potato | carrot | horse chestnut tree

Watching and recording runner beans grow

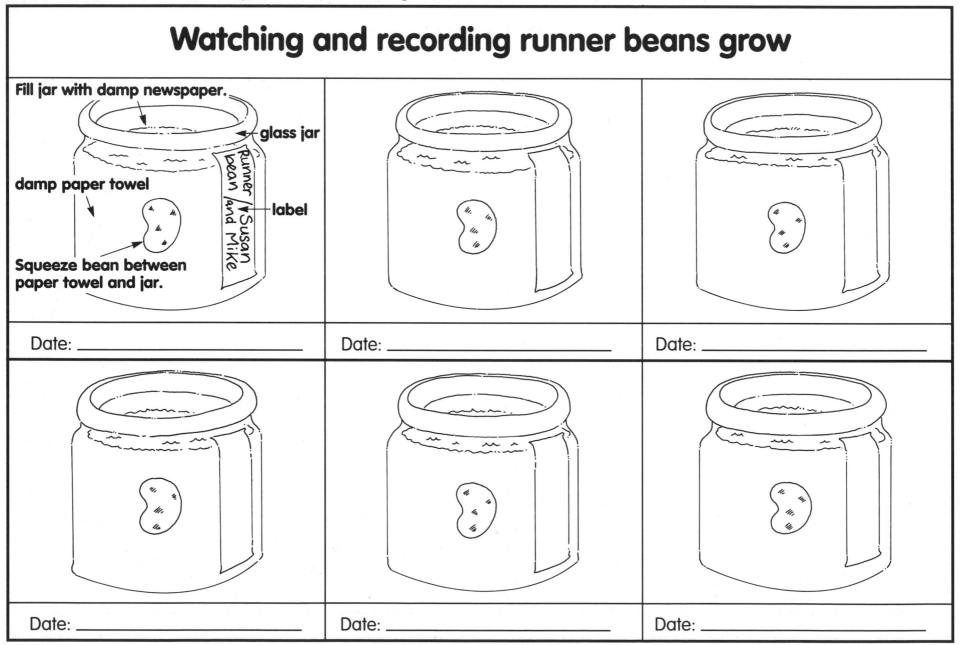

Fill jar with damp newspaper.

glass jar

damp paper towel

Runner bean / Susan and Mike

label

Squeeze bean between paper towel and jar.

Date: _____

Date: _____

Date: _____

Date: _____

Date: _____

Date: _____

Name _____

Sorting fruit

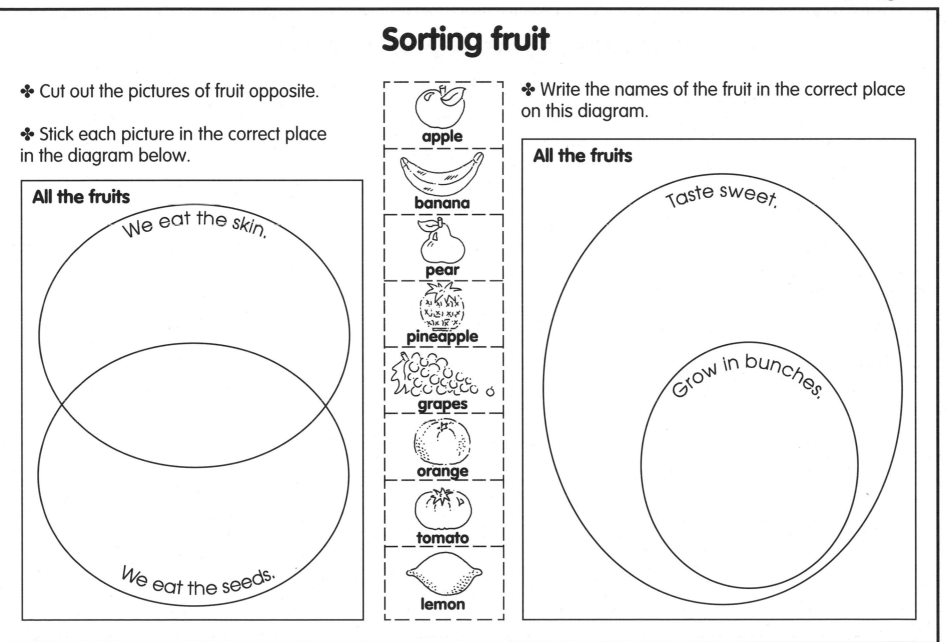

✤ Cut out the pictures of fruit opposite.

✤ Stick each picture in the correct place in the diagram below.

All the fruits

We eat the skin.

We eat the seeds.

apple

banana

pear

pineapple

grapes

orange

tomato

lemon

✤ Write the names of the fruit in the correct place on this diagram.

All the fruits

Taste sweet.

Grow in bunches.

Identifying fruit

❖ Cut out the pictures of fruit below.
❖ Put each fruit in the correct place on this page.

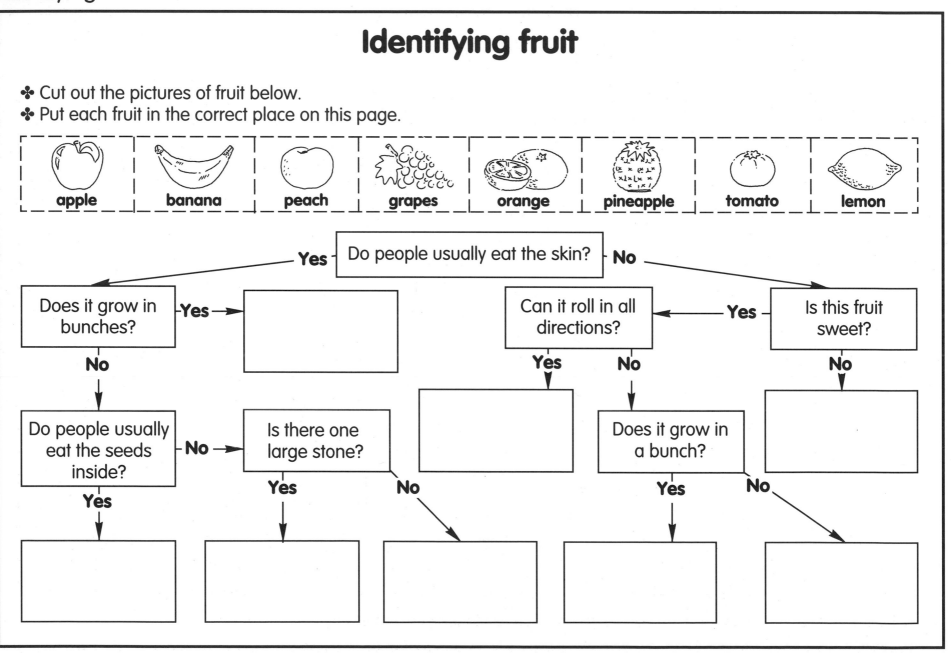

| apple | banana | peach | grapes | orange | pineapple | tomato | lemon |

Do people usually eat the skin?

Yes — Does it grow in bunches? — Yes →

No

Do people usually eat the seeds inside? — No → Is there one large stone?

Yes

Yes

No

No — Can it roll in all directions? — Yes — Is this fruit sweet?

Yes   No   No

Does it grow in a bunch?

Yes   No

Identifying leaves: 1

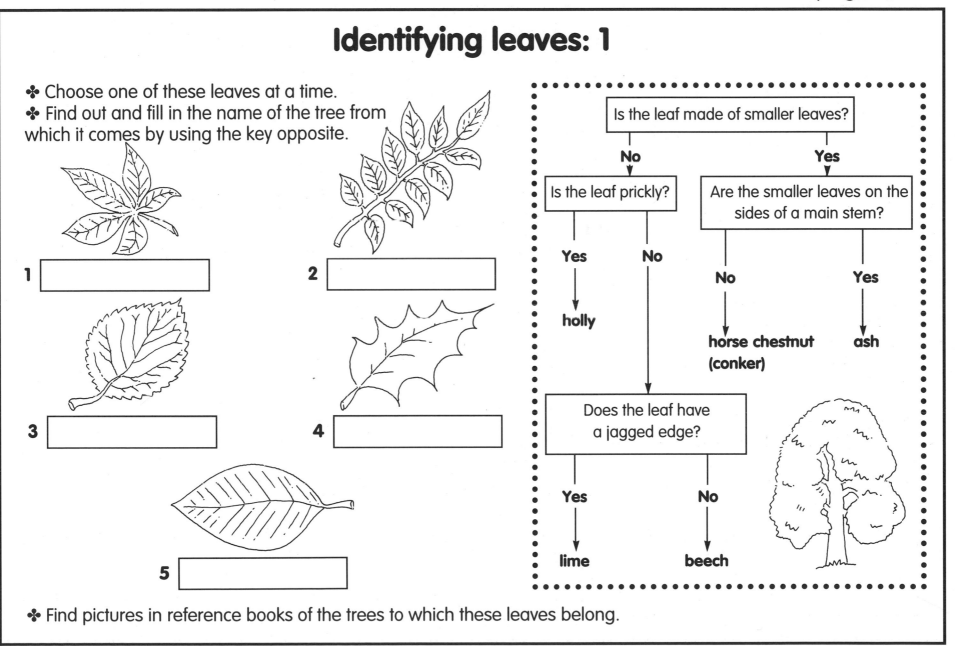

❧ Choose one of these leaves at a time.
❧ Find out and fill in the name of the tree from which it comes by using the key opposite.

1 [   ]

2 [   ]

3 [   ]

4 [   ]

5 [   ]

Is the leaf made of smaller leaves?

No → **Is the leaf prickly?**

Yes → **Are the smaller leaves on the sides of a main stem?**

Is the leaf prickly?
Yes → **holly**
No →

Are the smaller leaves on the sides of a main stem?
No → **horse chestnut (conker)**
Yes → **ash**

Does the leaf have a jagged edge?
Yes → **lime**
No → **beech**

❧ Find pictures in reference books of the trees to which these leaves belong.

Name _____

Eating plants

Some of the foods we eat come from plants. Different foods come from different parts of the plants.

❧ Look at these different foods. Decide from which part of their plants they come.

apple   carrot   celery   peas   tomato   cauliflower   sweetcorn   orange

radish   rhubarb   broccoli   lettuce   broad bean   cabbage   thyme   cucumber

♣ Complete the table below.

flower	stem	leaf	fruit	seed	root

Making food from plants

Much of the food we eat comes from plants – but which plants?

♣ Look at these foods from a shop.
♣ Draw a line from each food to the plant from which it comes.

OLIVE OIL

CORN FLAKES

Tomato Sauce

COCOA Powder

Marmalade

Self-Raising Flour

Long Grain RICE

Caster Sugar

JAM 1lb

PORRIDGE OATS

Pineapple Rings

BG TEA BAGS

COFFEE

Sunflower MARGARINE

Cooked Ham

Parts of a flowering plant

✤ Use the words in the box at the bottom of the page to label these drawings.

A plant germinating and beginning to grow	A fully grown plant	The flower

anther	bract	branch	filament	first leaves	flower	flower bud
lateral root	leaf stalk	leaf vein	main root	new seeds	ovary	petals
seed	sepals	shoot	stamen	stigma		

Identifying leaves: 2

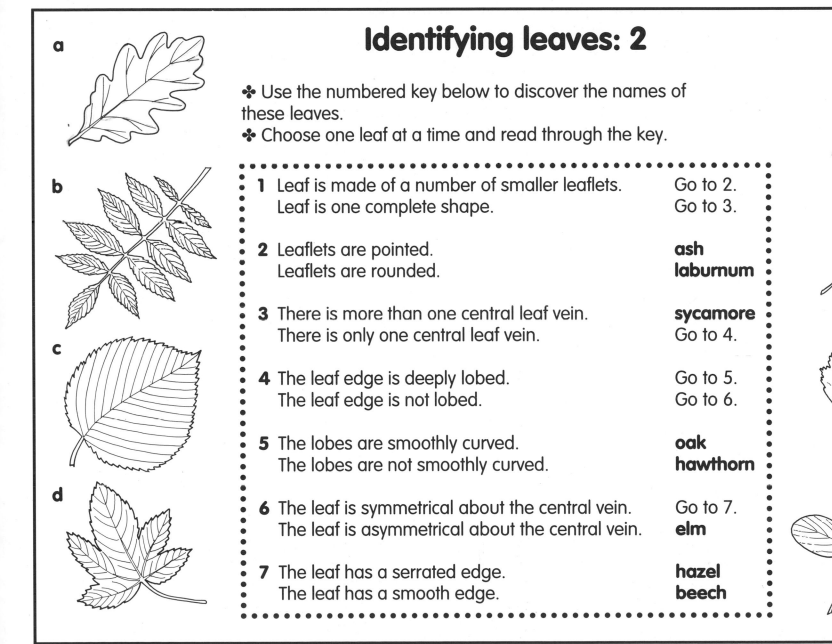

✤ Use the numbered key below to discover the names of these leaves.

✤ Choose one leaf at a time and read through the key.

1	Leaf is made of a number of smaller leaflets.	Go to 2.
	Leaf is one complete shape.	Go to 3.
2	Leaflets are pointed.	**ash**
	Leaflets are rounded.	**laburnum**
3	There is more than one central leaf vein.	**sycamore**
	There is only one central leaf vein.	Go to 4.
4	The leaf edge is deeply lobed.	Go to 5.
	The leaf edge is not lobed.	Go to 6.
5	The lobes are smoothly curved.	**oak**
	The lobes are not smoothly curved.	**hawthorn**
6	The leaf is symmetrical about the central vein.	Go to 7.
	The leaf is asymmetrical about the central vein.	**elm**
7	The leaf has a serrated edge.	**hazel**
	The leaf has a smooth edge.	**beech**

Making forces

Making forces

✤ Make some pushing forces.

| Push a book along a table. | Push a book along the carpet. | Push a door closed. | Push your body up from the floor. | Push against the classroom wall. |

✤ Make some pulling forces.

| Pull a drawer out. | Pull a book up from the floor. | Pull a door closed. | Pull a piece of rope. | Pull a piece of paper apart. |

✤ Write down: the three largest forces you used; the three smallest forces you used; and the two forces you made which **did not move** anything.

Muscles and forces

We move our bodies by making our muscles pull it into shape.

♣ Make a model of the muscles that move your foot.

You will need: a paper fastener, two elastic bands, cardboard, adhesive.

• Cut out these leg and foot shapes.

• Paste them on to thin card and cut them out.

• Punch out the holes carefully with a hole punch.

• Fix the shapes together as shown opposite.

♣ Make your model work by stretching outwards one of the elastic bands.

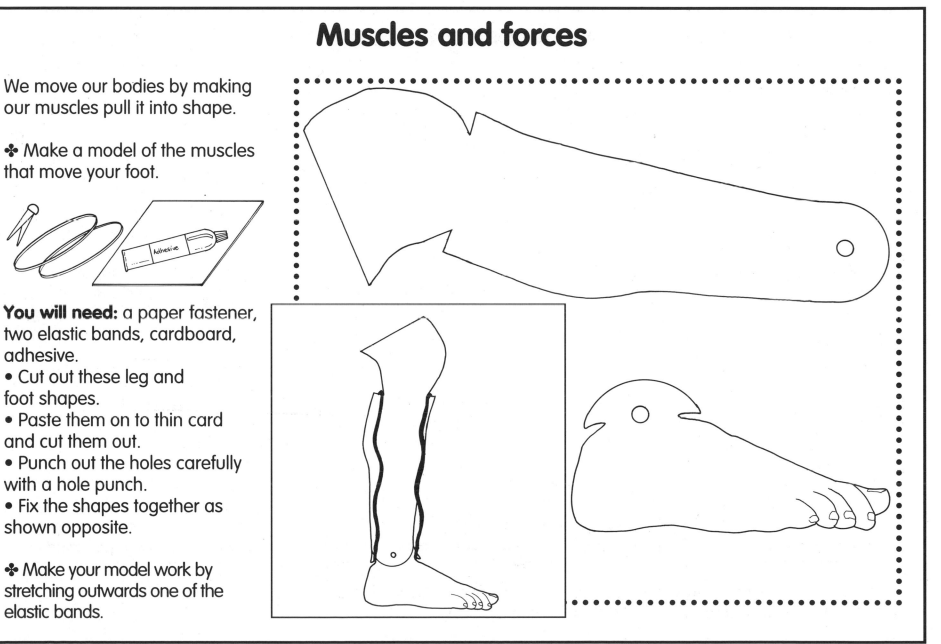

Name _____

Marbles and moving air

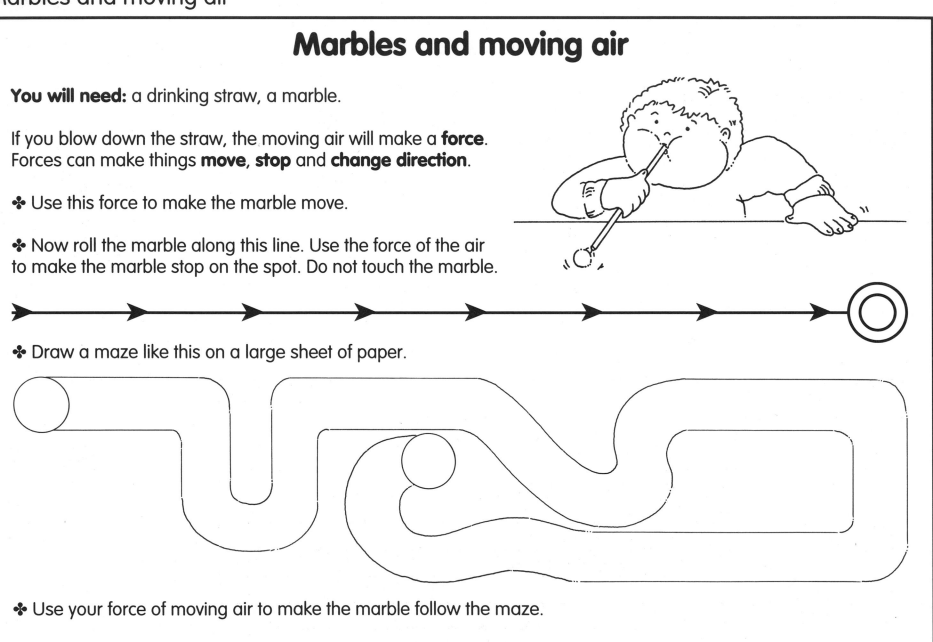

Marbles and moving air

You will need: a drinking straw, a marble.

If you blow down the straw, the moving air will make a **force**. Forces can make things **move**, **stop** and **change direction**.

❖ Use this force to make the marble move.

❖ Now roll the marble along this line. Use the force of the air to make the marble stop on the spot. Do not touch the marble.

❖ Draw a maze like this on a large sheet of paper.

❖ Use your force of moving air to make the marble follow the maze.

Measuring forces

❖ Make this simple **force meter**.

You will need: thick card, string, a ruler, an elastic band.

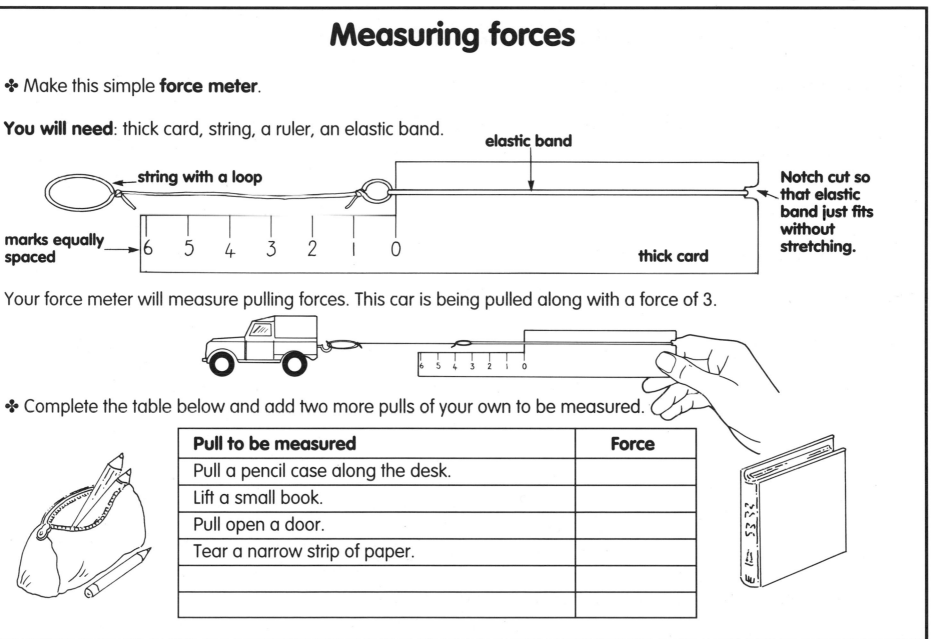

string with a loop

elastic band

Notch cut so that elastic band just fits without stretching.

marks equally spaced → 6 5 4 3 2 1 0

thick card

Your force meter will measure pulling forces. This car is being pulled along with a force of 3.

6 5 4 3 2 1 0

❖ Complete the table below and add two more pulls of your own to be measured.

Pull to be measured	Force
Pull a pencil case along the desk.	
Lift a small book.	
Pull open a door.	
Tear a narrow strip of paper.	

Name _____

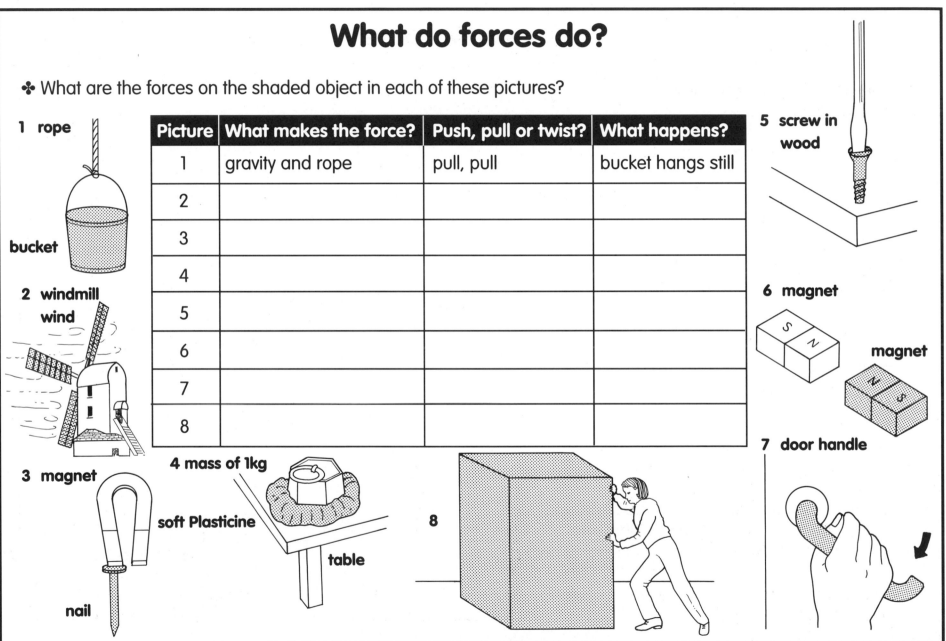

What do forces do?

❧ What are the forces on the shaded object in each of these pictures?

1 rope

bucket

2 windmill
wind

3 magnet

nail

4 mass of 1kg

soft Plasticine

table

8

5 screw in wood

6 magnet

magnet

7 door handle

Picture	What makes the force?	Push, pull or twist?	What happens?
1	gravity and rope	pull, pull	bucket hangs still
2			
3			
4			
5			
6			
7			
8			

Magnetic force

♣ Make a simple **swingometer** as shown below.

You will need: drawing pin, string, Plasticine, paper clip, a selection of magnets.

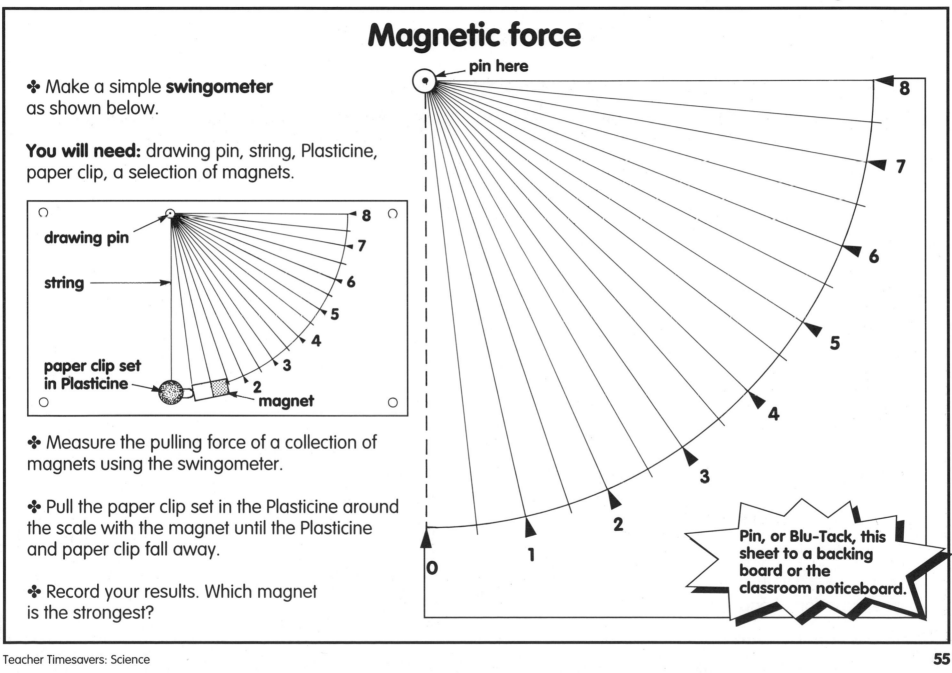

♣ Measure the pulling force of a collection of magnets using the swingometer.

♣ Pull the paper clip set in the Plasticine around the scale with the magnet until the Plasticine and paper clip fall away.

♣ Record your results. Which magnet is the strongest?

Pin, or Blu-Tack, this sheet to a backing board or the classroom noticeboard.

Force meters: 1

Force meters: 1

❖ Write down the force shown on each of these **force meters**.

❖ Find an object in the classroom which might be hanging on each force meter
to give these force readings.

Force meters: 2

♣ Record the force shown on each of these force meters. Forces are measured in **newtons (N)**.

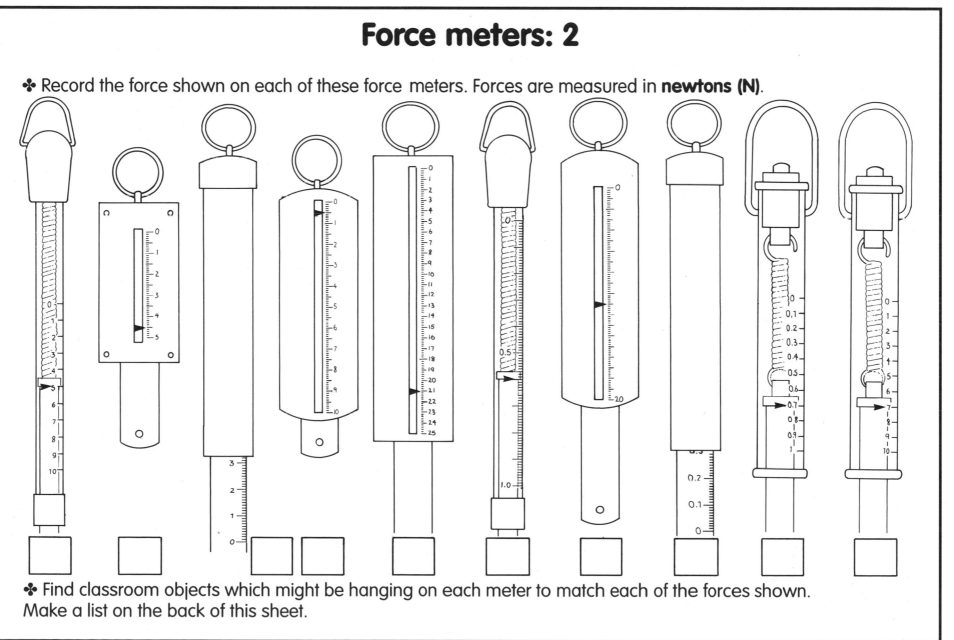

♣ Find classroom objects which might be hanging on each meter to match each of the forces shown.
Make a list on the back of this sheet.

Water can push

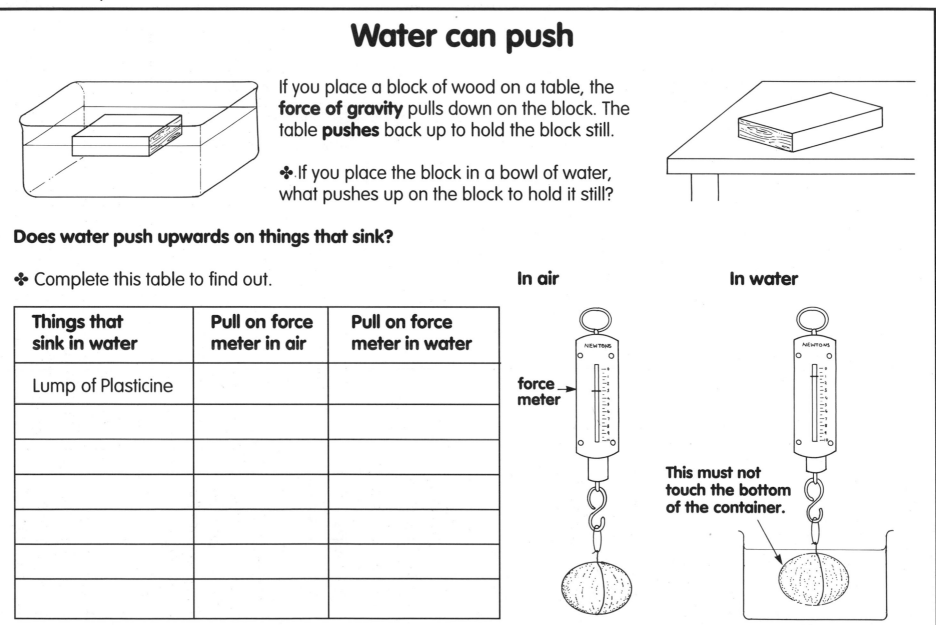

Water can push

If you place a block of wood on a table, the **force of gravity** pulls down on the block. The table **pushes** back up to hold the block still.

❖ If you place the block in a bowl of water, what pushes up on the block to hold it still?

Does water push upwards on things that sink?

❖ Complete this table to find out.

Things that sink in water	Pull on force meter in air	Pull on force meter in water
Lump of Plasticine		

In air

force meter

In water

This must not touch the bottom of the container.

Bouncing balls

Bouncing balls

❖ Watch a ball bounce.

1 Here **gravity** pulls down on the ball and starts it moving.

2 Here the ball is moving faster. The force of gravity remains the same.

3 Here the ball squashes into a new shape and the floor squashes a bit too! During the bounce the ball and floor spring back into shape, pushing the ball upwards with a force.

4 The force of gravity is trying to slow the ball down now.

5 At last gravity succeeds in stopping the ball going up, and it starts to fall again.

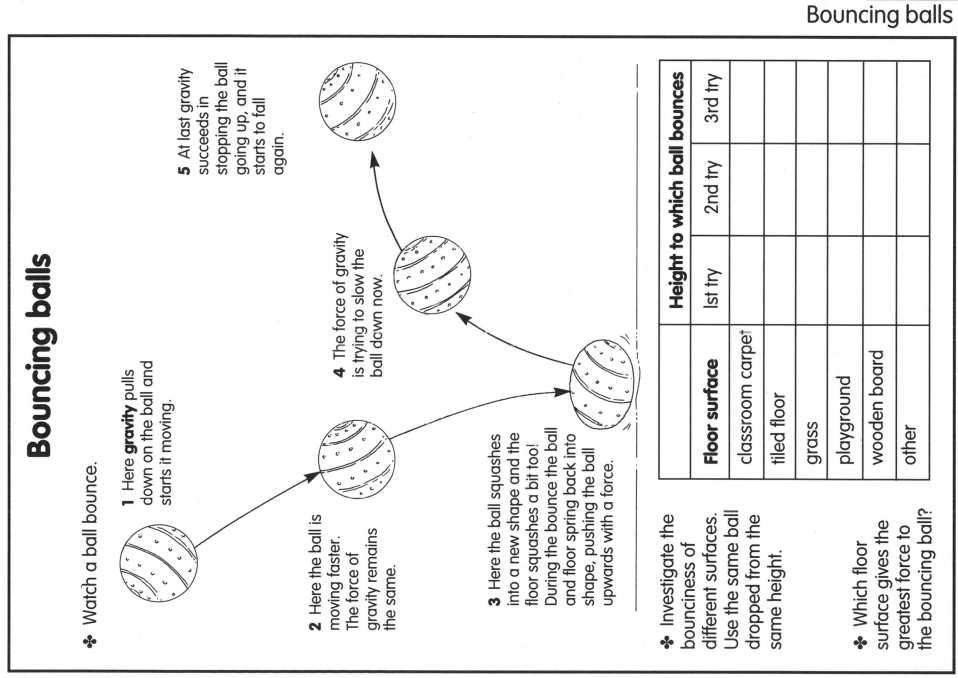

Floor surface	Height to which ball bounces		
	1st try	2nd try	3rd try
classroom carpet			
tiled floor			
grass			
playground			
wooden board			
other			

❖ Investigate the bounciness of different surfaces. Use the same ball dropped from the same height.

❖ Which floor surface gives the greatest force to the bouncing ball?

Name _____

Friction – friend or foe?

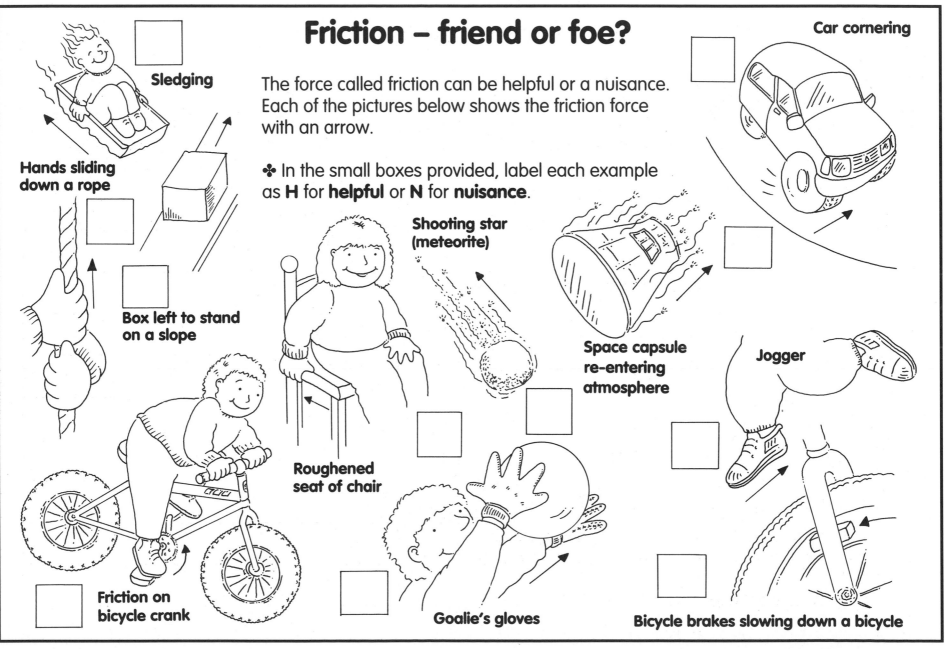

Friction – friend or foe?

The force called friction can be helpful or a nuisance. Each of the pictures below shows the friction force with an arrow.

✤ In the small boxes provided, label each example as **H** for **helpful** or **N** for **nuisance**.

Sledging

Hands sliding down a rope

Box left to stand on a slope

Shooting star (meteorite)

Space capsule re-entering atmosphere

Car cornering

Jogger

Friction on bicycle crank

Roughened seat of chair

Goalie's gloves

Bicycle brakes slowing down a bicycle

Bicycle gears

When you pedal a bicycle your legs push with a force on the pedals. The gears help you to push with different forces.

♣ Investigate the force needed to make the wheels turn in different gears.

• Turn a bicycle upside down.

The force you are using is used to overcome the friction in the bicycle parts. Is your bicycle well oiled?

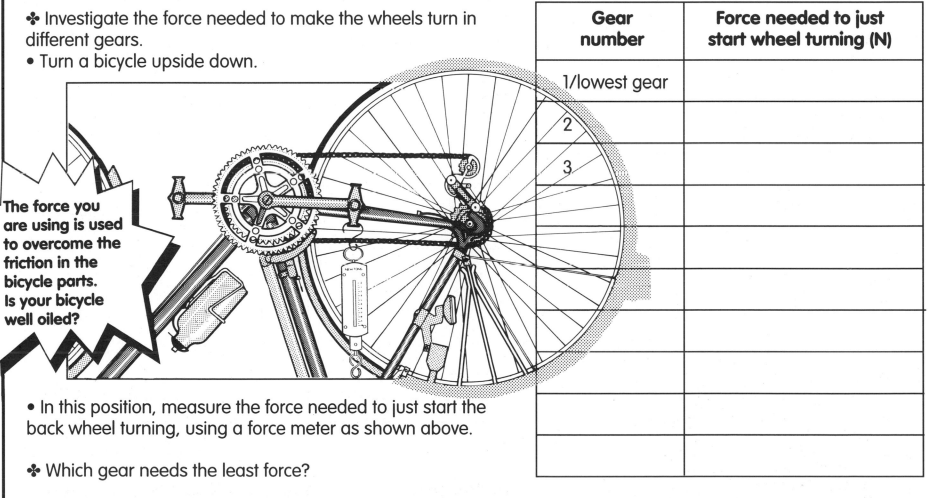

• In this position, measure the force needed to just start the back wheel turning, using a force meter as shown above.

♣ Which gear needs the least force?

• Now fill in this table to suit the number of gears on your bicycle.

Gear number	Force needed to just start wheel turning (N)
1/lowest gear	
2	
3	

Energy can be dangerous

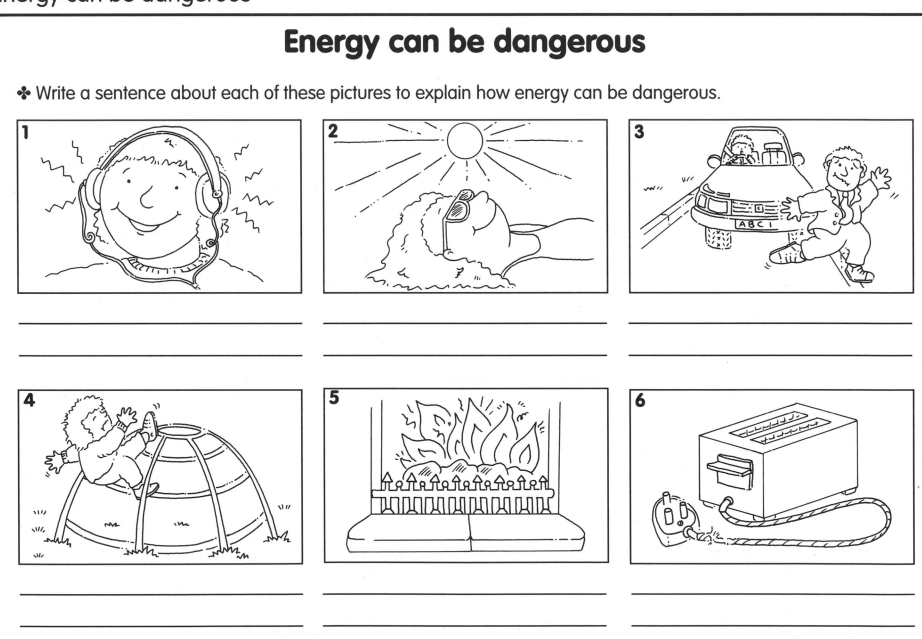

Energy can be dangerous

♣ Write a sentence about each of these pictures to explain how energy can be dangerous.

Booby trap

Take care!

Elastic bands store energy when they are stretched or twisted.

❖ Make a **booby trap** to startle your friends as shown below.

You will need: elastic bands, headless matchsticks.

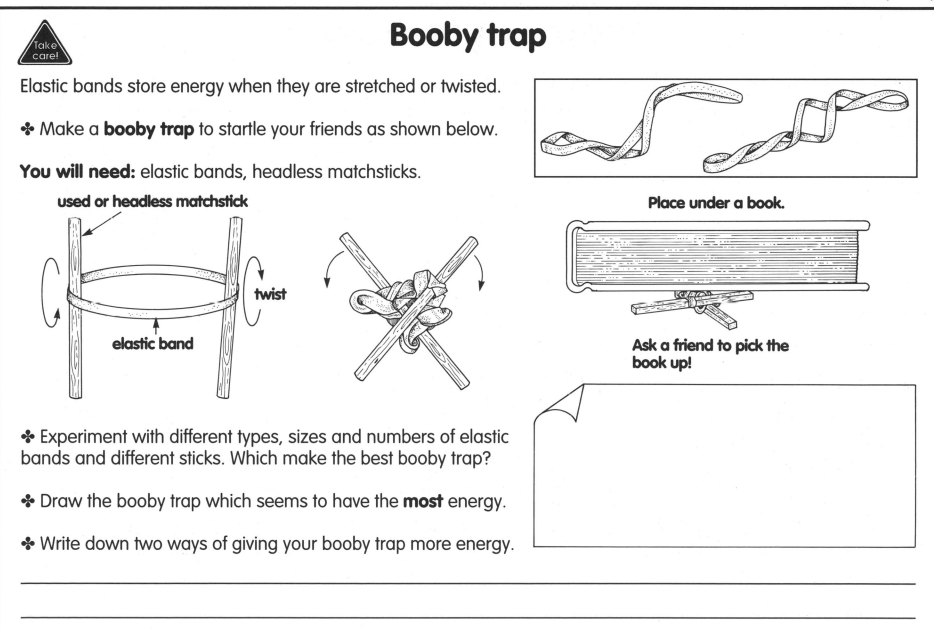

used or headless matchstick

twist

elastic band

Place under a book.

Ask a friend to pick the book up!

❖ Experiment with different types, sizes and numbers of elastic bands and different sticks. Which make the best booby trap?

❖ Draw the booby trap which seems to have the **most** energy.

❖ Write down two ways of giving your booby trap more energy.

Name _____

Toy car on a slope

Toy car on a slope

Thin board is best!

A toy car on a slope has the energy to roll down.
What happens when it is given more and more energy?

tape measure

♣ Make a slope so that a toy car can roll down and along the floor.

You will need: thin board, a tape measure, a toy car, something to raise one end of the board.

♣ Start the toy car from different places on the slope and measure how far the car rolls along the floor each time.

Fill in the table below.

Where does the car start (cm up the slope)?	How far along the floor does the car roll (cm)?

♣ Where does the toy car have the most energy?

♣ Can you think of other ways of giving the car more energy? On the back of this sheet, draw pictures to show how this could be done.

Water-wheels

The energy in moving water can turn a water-wheel or turbine. The water-wheel can drive machinery to grind corn or make electrical energy.

✤ Make a simple water-wheel as shown opposite.

You will need: a drawing pin, 15cm length of dowelling, Plasticine, plastic drink bottle.

✤ Pour water from a jug on to the blades of the water-wheel.

As the water-wheel gets more energy from the water it will turn faster.

✤ How can you make this happen?

✤ Find out if bigger blades help the wheel to turn faster. Make a fair comparison between the first blades and larger ones.

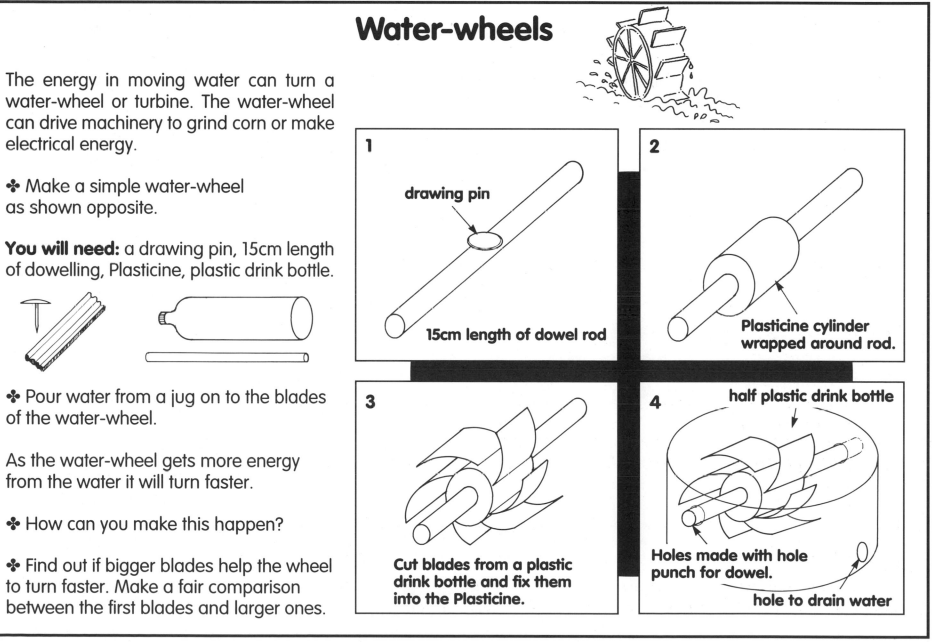

1 drawing pin

15cm length of dowel rod

2 Plasticine cylinder wrapped around rod.

3 Cut blades from a plastic drink bottle and fix them into the Plasticine.

4 half plastic drink bottle

Holes made with hole punch for dowel.

hole to drain water

Name _____

Ice cold

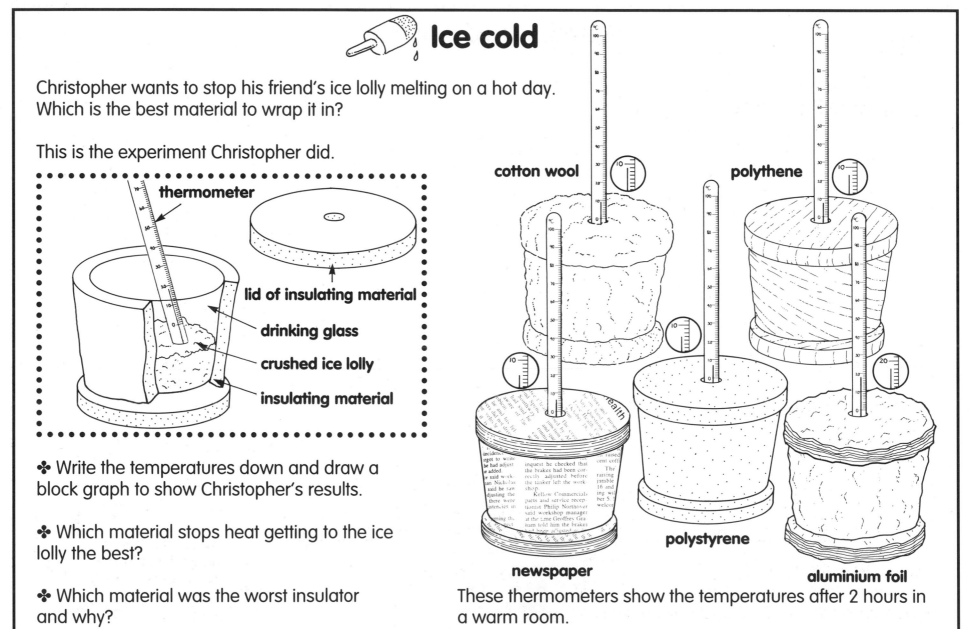

Ice cold

Christopher wants to stop his friend's ice lolly melting on a hot day. Which is the best material to wrap it in?

This is the experiment Christopher did.

thermometer

lid of insulating material

drinking glass

crushed ice lolly

insulating material

cotton wool

polythene

polystyrene

newspaper

aluminium foil

♣ Write the temperatures down and draw a block graph to show Christopher's results.

♣ Which material stops heat getting to the ice lolly the best?

♣ Which material was the worst insulator and why?

These thermometers show the temperatures after 2 hours in a warm room.

Spirals and candles

Take care!

Candle wax has energy stored in it.
Energy is needed to make things move.

❧ Change the energy in candle wax into the energy in a moving spiral.

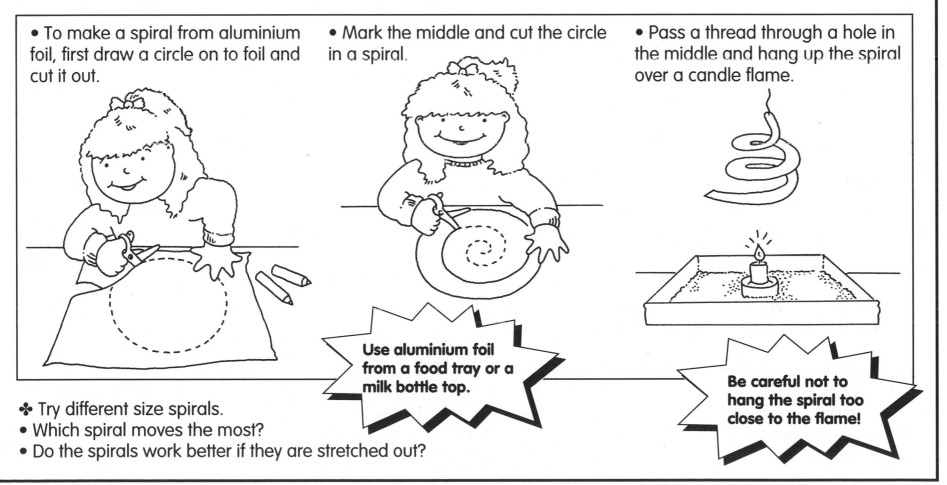

• To make a spiral from aluminium foil, first draw a circle on to foil and cut it out.

• Mark the middle and cut the circle in a spiral.

• Pass a thread through a hole in the middle and hang up the spiral over a candle flame.

Use aluminium foil from a food tray or a milk bottle top.

Be careful not to hang the spiral too close to the flame!

❧ Try different size spirals.
• Which spiral moves the most?
• Do the spirals work better if they are stretched out?

Energy from oil

Oil forms under the Earth's surface. We get petrol from oil. A car needs the energy stored in petrol to make it move.

♣ Look at these pictures and captions. They tell how oil is formed. However, they are jumbled up.

♣ Cut out the pictures and captions and put them together in the correct order.

Thick layers of rock gradually formed over these remains.

Heat and pressure turned the remains into oil.

The oil was trapped by rocks. A hole has to be drilled to get it out.

Their bones and shells were gradually covered by mud and sand.

The tiny plants and animals living in the sea millions of years ago fell to the seabed when they died.

Cooling a hot drink

The pictures below show the same cup of hot chocolate as it cools down.

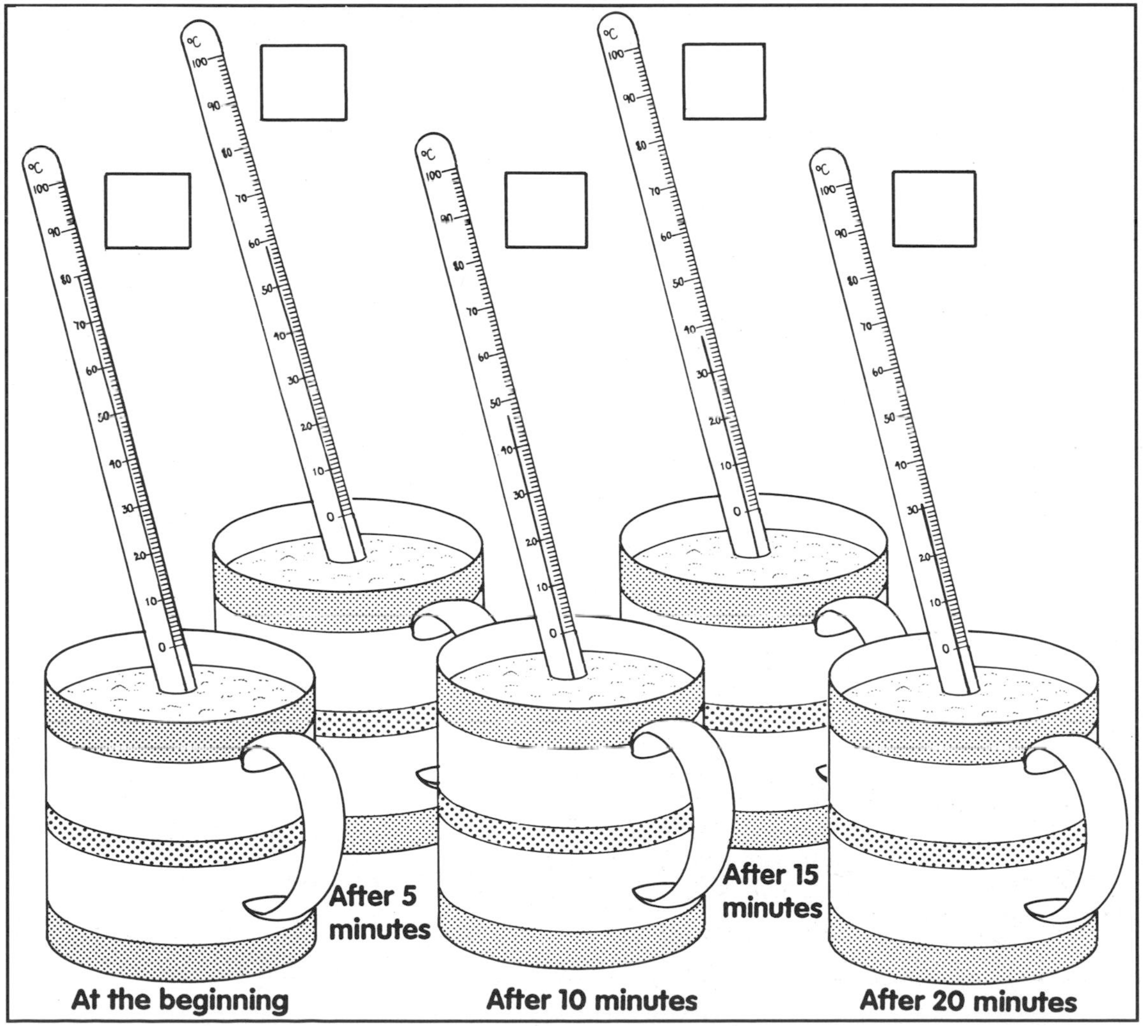

❖ Write the correct temperature in each small box and fill in the graph.

❖ What would you predict the temperature of the drink to be after 25 minutes? [ ] °C

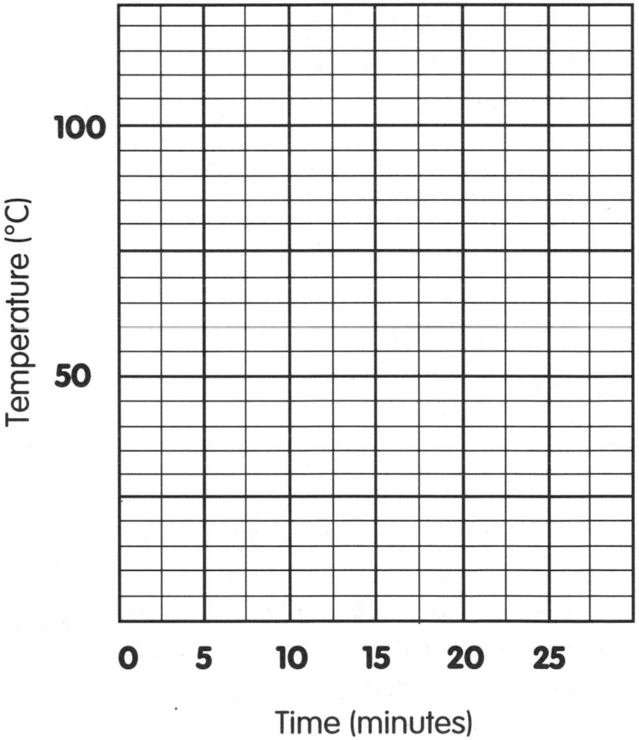

At the beginning

After 5 minutes

After 10 minutes

After 15 minutes

After 20 minutes

Temperature (°C)

100

50

0   5   10   15   20   25

Time (minutes)

Balloon rocket

Balloon rocket

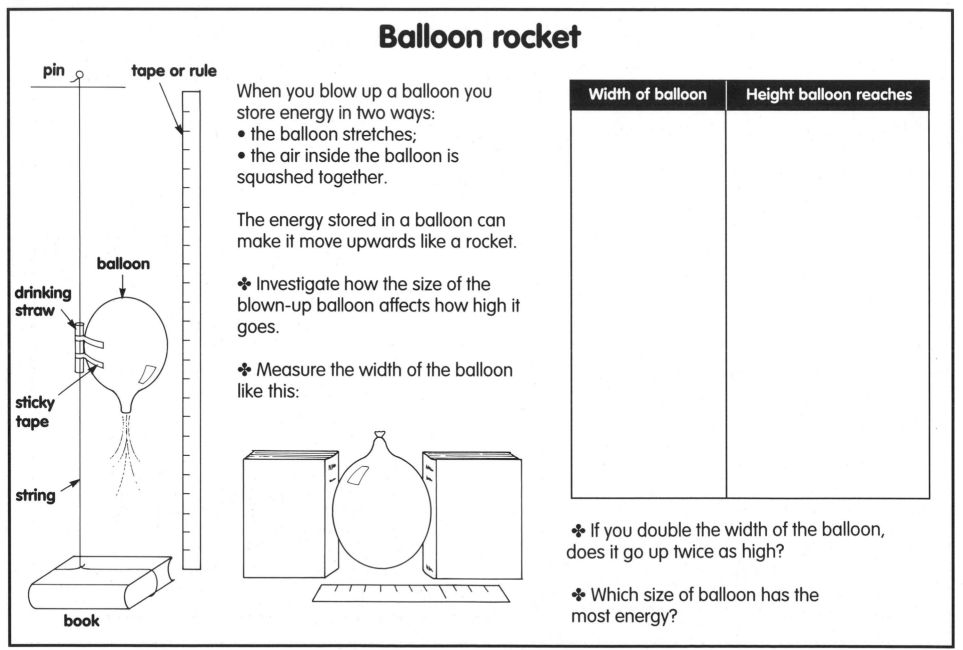

pin

tape or rule

balloon

drinking
straw

sticky
tape

string

book

When you blow up a balloon you store energy in two ways:
• the balloon stretches;
• the air inside the balloon is squashed together.

The energy stored in a balloon can make it move upwards like a rocket.

❧ Investigate how the size of the blown-up balloon affects how high it goes.

❧ Measure the width of the balloon like this:

Width of balloon	Height balloon reaches

❧ If you double the width of the balloon, does it go up twice as high?

❧ Which size of balloon has the most energy?

Make a mouse

A twisted elastic band can store energy.

♣ Make a 'mouse' powered by an elastic band.

You will need: elastic band, cotton reel, headless matchsticks, plastic drink bottle, string, paper clips, sticky tape.

• Fix an elastic band through the middle of the cotton reel by inserting some short lengths of dowel or matchstick.
• Assemble the 'mouse' as shown opposite.
• Pull the string and release the 'mouse'.

♣ Find out what happens if:
• you run the mouse on several different surfaces;
• you use different elastic bands;
• you make the cotton reel heavier by filling it with Plasticine.

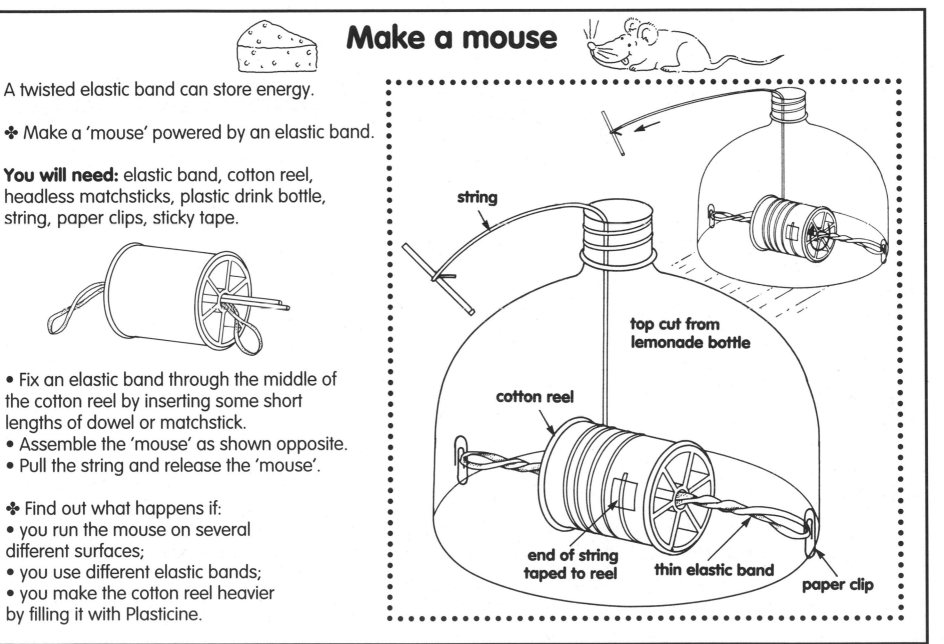

string

top cut from lemonade bottle

cotton reel

end of string taped to reel

thin elastic band

paper clip

Name _____

DANGER – Electricity!

Electricity can be dangerous.
♣ Colour in red all the areas of danger in this picture.
♣ On the back of this sheet, explain why each area is dangerous
and how the danger could be avoided.

Lighting the bulb

You will need: a battery, some wire and a bulb.

✤ Find out which of these circuits will light the bulb.

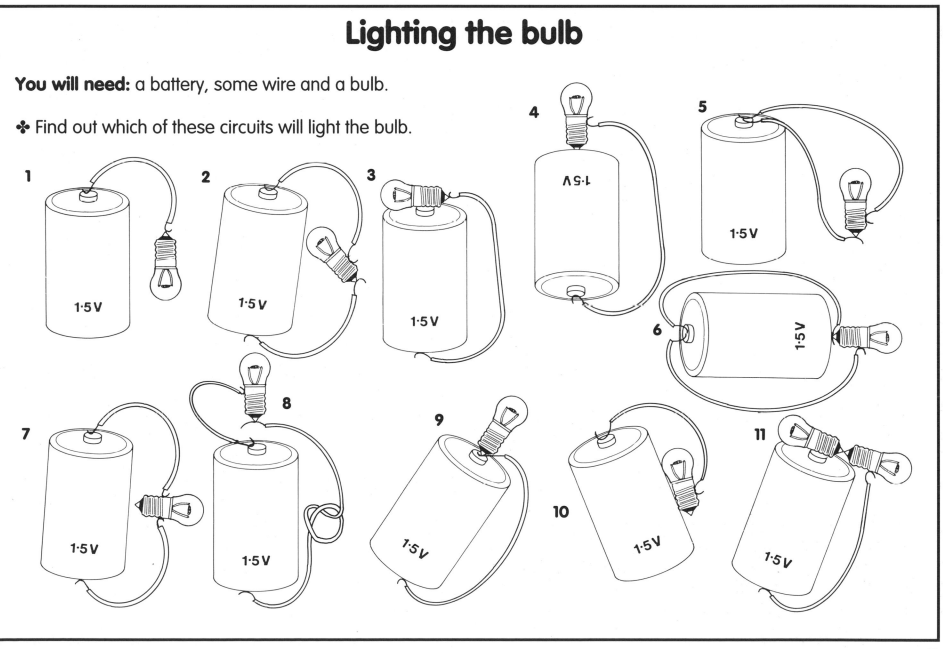

Making it flow

♣ Which materials conduct electricity (that is, let it flow through them)? Carry out this investigation to find out.

You will need: a battery, a bulb in a holder, some wires with crocodile connectors.

1 Make an electrical circuit to light a bulb, as shown below.
2 Now add an extra crocodile connector wire to your circuit.

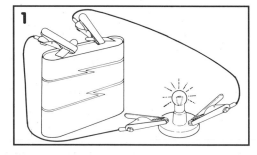 

3 Collect some things made with different materials; for example: aluminium foil, string, polythene, an iron key, a brass screw, an elastic band, a plastic pen top, water, a coin, stainless steel, wood, a wire pipe cleaner or pencil 'lead'.

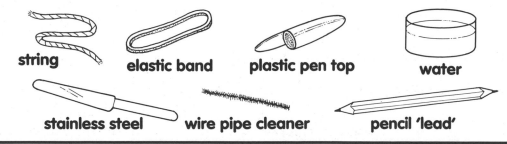

string   **elastic band**   **plastic pen top**   **water**

stainless steel   **wire pipe cleaner**   **pencil 'lead'**

4 Clip each of these things in turn between the crocodile connectors. Does the electricity still flow to the bulb?

5 Complete this table to record your results.

Object	Made of:	Conducts electricity?
foil	aluminium	

♣ What do you notice about the things that conduct electricity?

Name _____

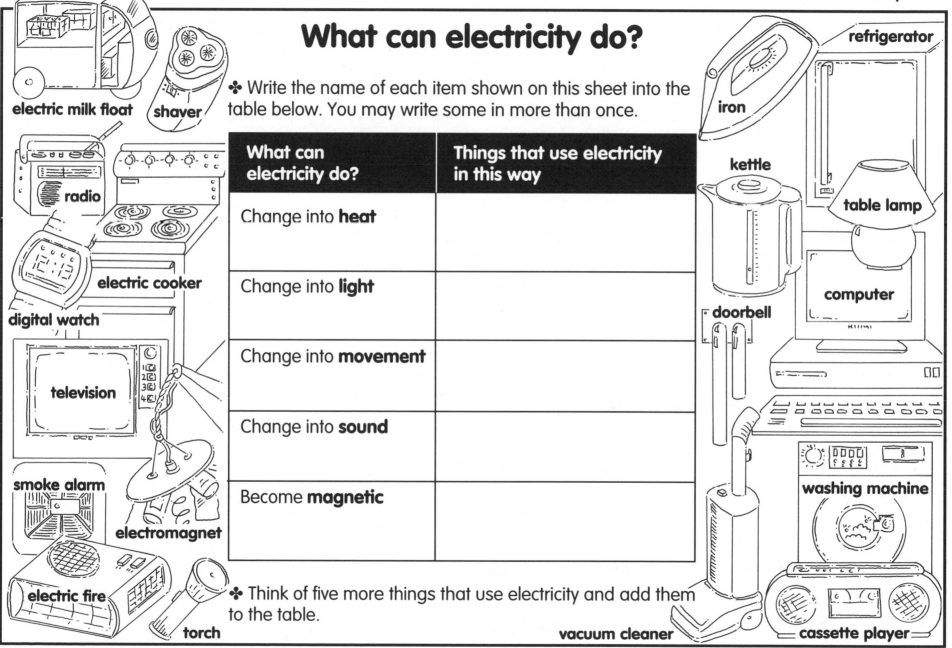

What can electricity do?

♣ Write the name of each item shown on this sheet into the table below. You may write some in more than once.

electric milk float

shaver

radio

electric cooker

digital watch

television

smoke alarm

electromagnet

electric fire

torch

iron

refrigerator

kettle

table lamp

doorbell

computer

washing machine

vacuum cleaner

cassette player

What can electricity do?	Things that use electricity in this way
Change into **heat**	
Change into **light**	
Change into **movement**	
Change into **sound**	
Become **magnetic**	

♣ Think of five more things that use electricity and add them to the table.

Inventing diagrams

Name _____

Inventing diagrams

♣ Make a circuit to light a bulb.

You will need: a battery, some wires with crocodile connectors, a bulb in a holder.

♣ Carefully, draw a picture of your circuit in the box opposite.

Instead of drawing a battery, it might be easier to have a simple symbol. For example:

battery = ☐   or battery = ⬭ ○ ○ ⬭

♣ On the back of this sheet, make up and draw symbols for a battery, a bulb, some wire, and a switch.

♣ Now draw these circuits using your symbols:

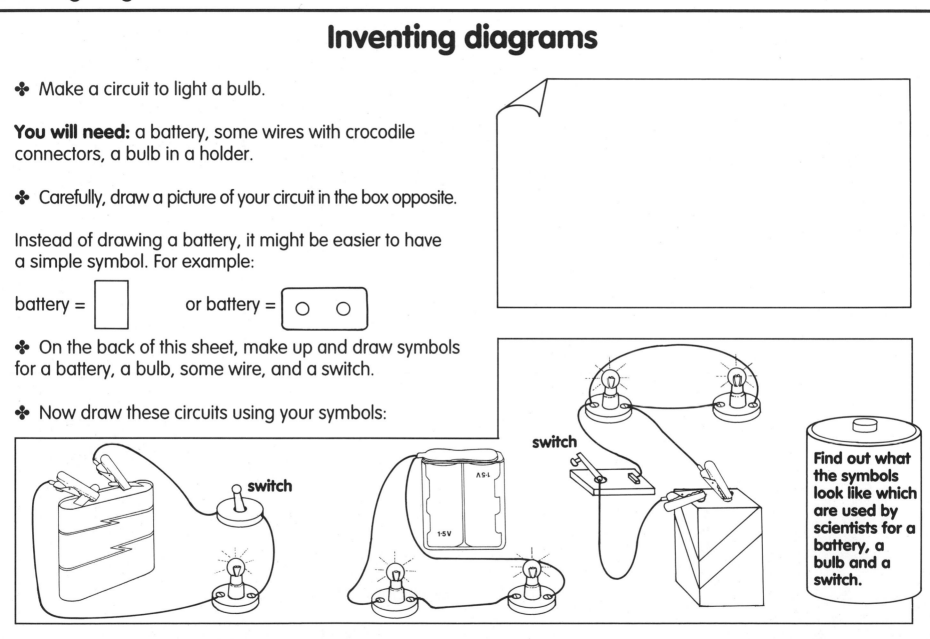

switch

switch

Find out what the symbols look like which are used by scientists for a battery, a bulb and a switch.

Sending messages

✤ Make a circuit in order to send a Morse code message to your friend. Write down your message first.

You will need: a battery, a bulb in a holder or a buzzer, some wires with crocodile connectors.

Morse code

A	•—	N	—•
B	—•••	O	———
C	—•—•	P	•——•
D	—••	Q	——•—
E	•	R	•—•
F	••—•	S	•••
G	——•	T	—
H	••••	U	••—
I	••	V	•••—
J	•———	W	•——
K	—•—	X	—••—
L	•—••	Y	—•——
M	——	Z	——••

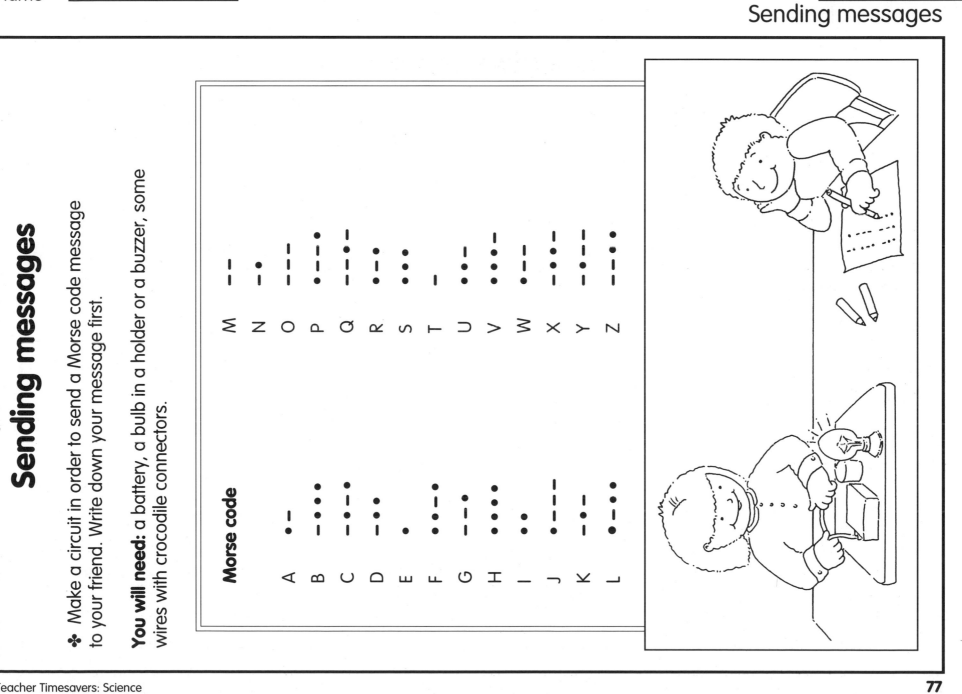

Electric motor

Electric motor

♣ Find out how an electric motor works in different circuits.

You will need: 1.5V battery, a bulb, some wires with crocodile connectors, an electric motor, a small cardboard circle.

♣ Fill in this observation table.

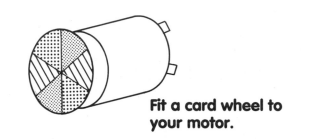

Fit a card wheel to your motor.

Circuit	Circuit diagram	Observations
Connect one battery to the motor.		
Turn the battery the other way round.		
Change over the motor terminals.		
Connect two batteries to the motor.		
Add one bulb to the circuit.		
With two batteries, include a short pencil in the circuit.		

Making switches

❧ Make the electrical circuit shown below.

You will need: a battery, a bulb in a holder, some wires with crocodile connectors.

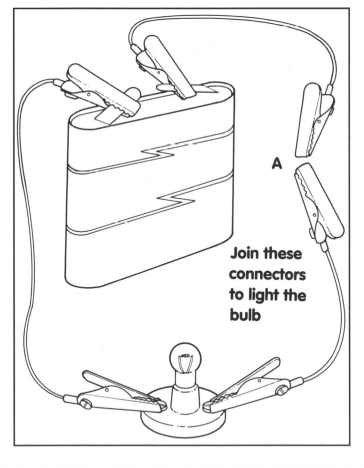

A

Join these connectors to light the bulb

❧ Now make the switches shown below.

You will need: cardboard, adhesive, aluminium foil, paper fasteners,

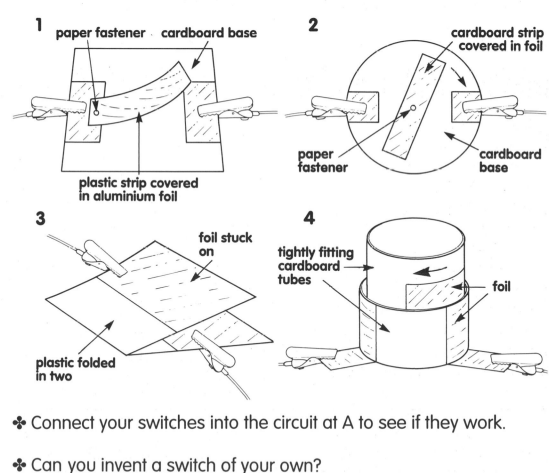

1 paper fastener · cardboard base

plastic strip covered in aluminium foil

2 cardboard strip covered in foil

paper fastener

cardboard base

3 foil stuck on

plastic folded in two

4 tightly fitting cardboard tubes

foil

❧ Connect your switches into the circuit at A to see if they work.

❧ Can you invent a switch of your own?

Electromagnetism

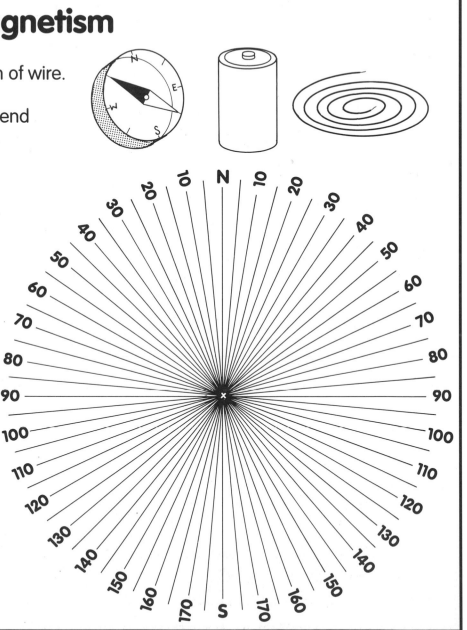

You will need: a magnetic compass, a battery, about 50cm of wire.

♣ Lay part of the wire over the compass and connect each end to the battery for a few seconds. What happens?
A wire with electricity running through it becomes magnetic too.

♣ Now try this experiment.
• Place your compass at X and turn **this page** until the needle points to (north) N.
• Wind the wire **once** around the compass in the direction (north-south) NS.
• Connect the ends of the wire to the battery for a few seconds. Where does the compass needle turn to?
• Repeat this with more winds of the wire around the compass. Each time you add a wind of wire record the result in the table below.

Number of winds	Angle needle turns through

♣ Discuss your results with a friend. What do you notice?

Name _____

Clown's face

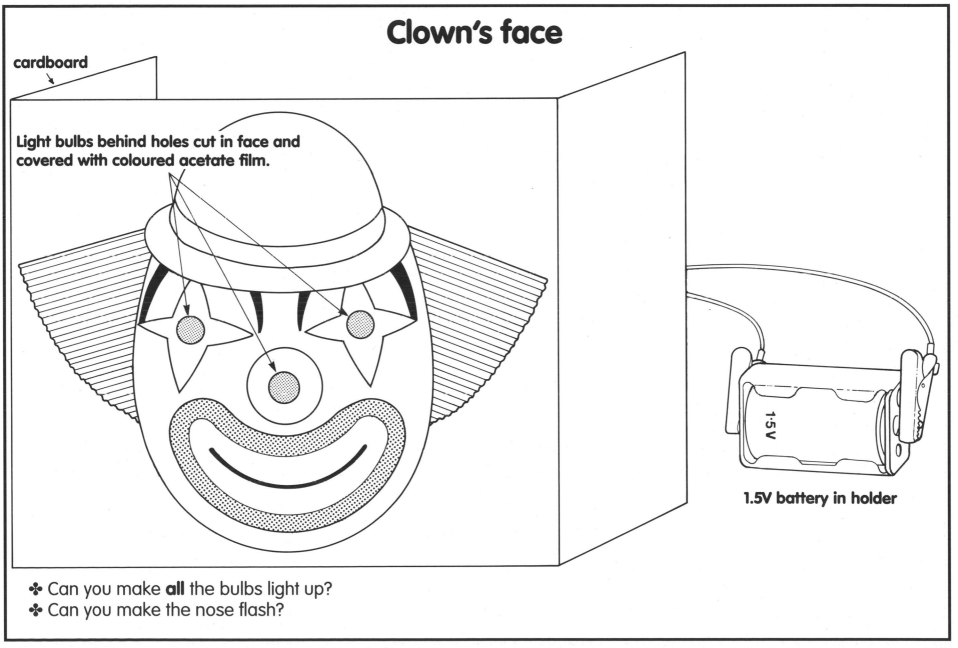

cardboard

Light bulbs behind holes cut in face and covered with coloured acetate film.

1·5 V

1.5V battery in holder

❧ Can you make **all** the bulbs light up?
❧ Can you make the nose flash?

Wheel of fortune

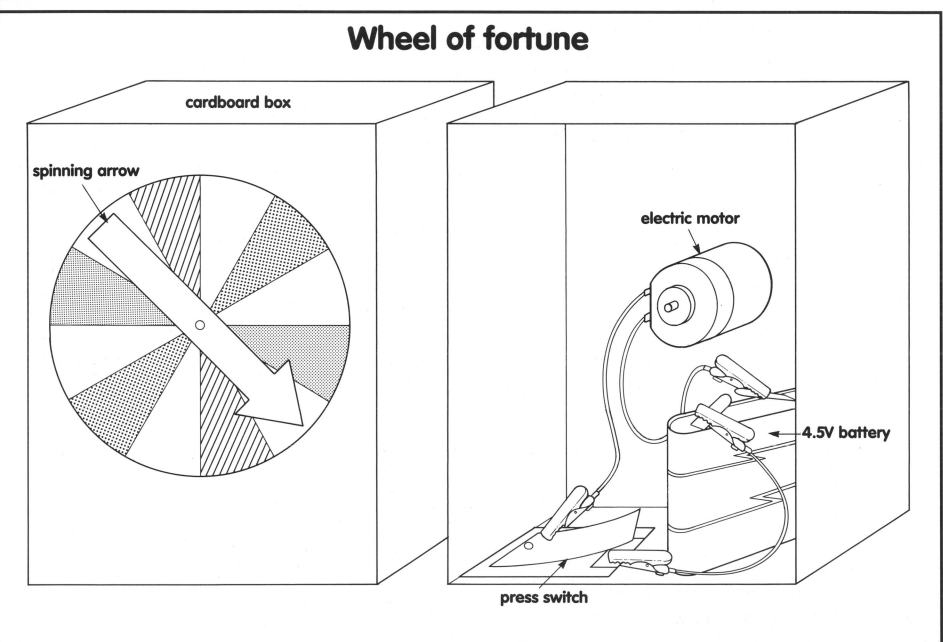

cardboard box

spinning arrow

electric motor

4.5V battery

press switch

Pressure pad

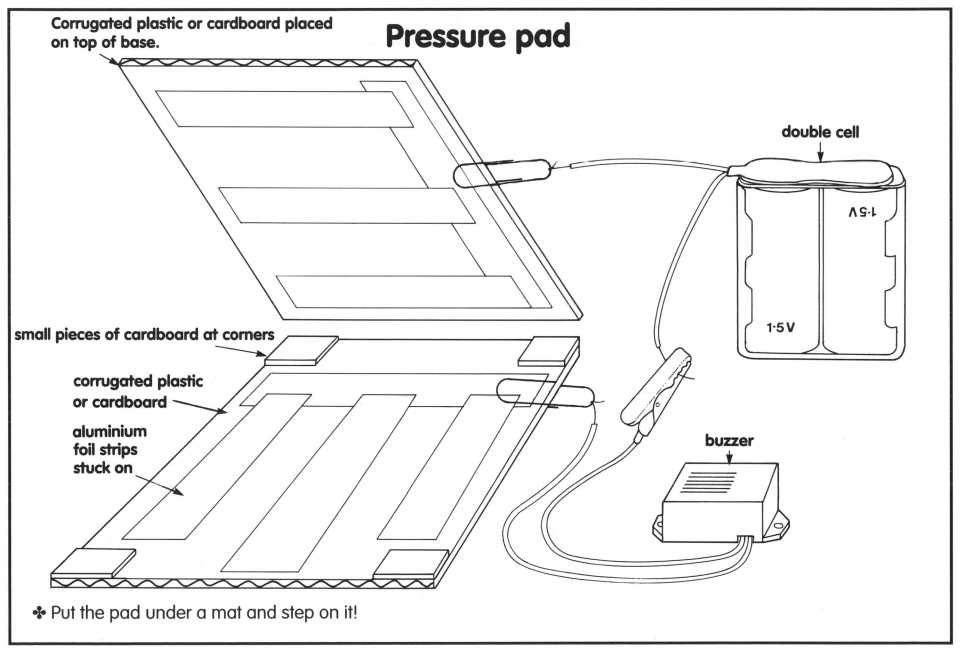

Corrugated plastic or cardboard placed on top of base.

double cell

1·5 V

1·5 V

small pieces of cardboard at corners

corrugated plastic or cardboard

aluminium foil strips stuck on

buzzer

♣ Put the pad under a mat and step on it!

Name _____

Car-park barrier

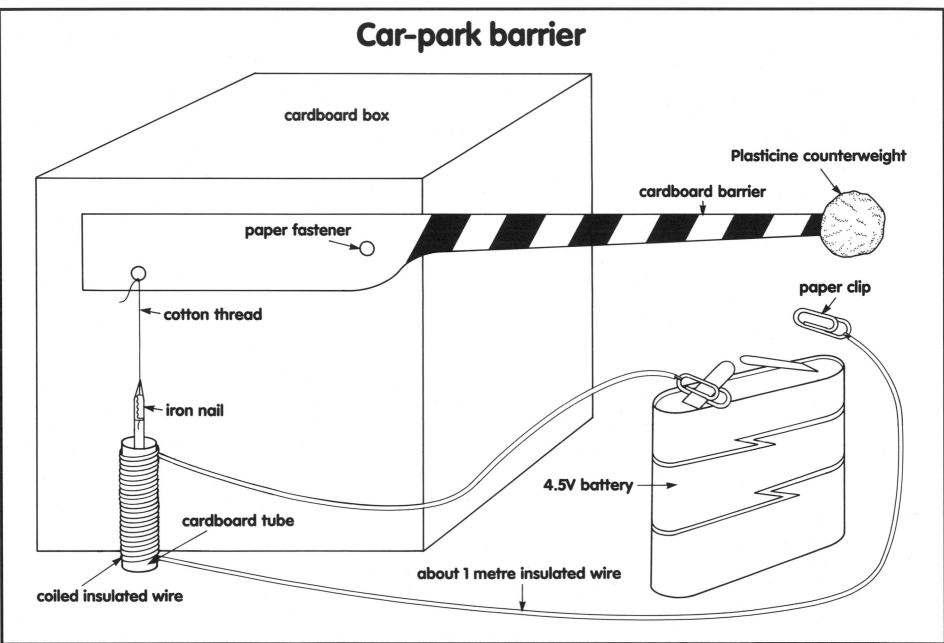

cardboard box

Plasticine counterweight

cardboard barrier

paper fastener

cotton thread

iron nail

paper clip

4.5V battery

cardboard tube

coiled insulated wire

about 1 metre insulated wire

Rainbow

The colours of the rainbow are: red, orange, yellow, green, blue, indigo (dark blue) and violet.

✤ Colour this rainbow carefully.

✤ Draw a picture under your rainbow.

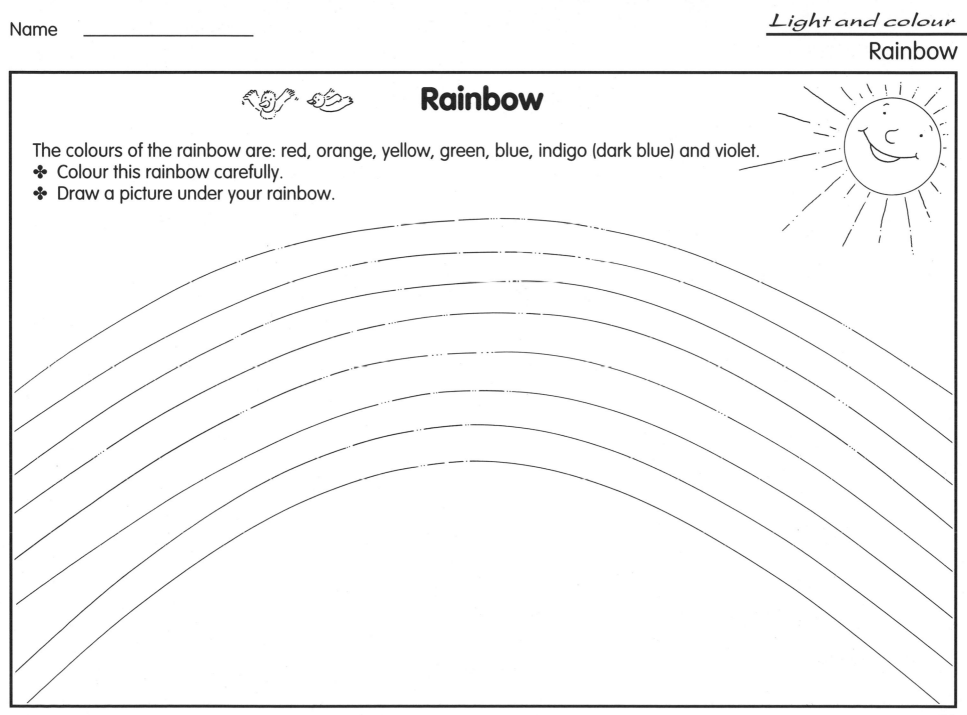

Making shadows

You will need: a torch, a one pence coin.
❧ Try to make shadows like these with your torch and the coin.

❧ Now make three different shadows of your own with the coin and draw them below.

♣ Make a challenge for your friend:
● Find a simple shape: a square of card or a cube or a drawing pin.

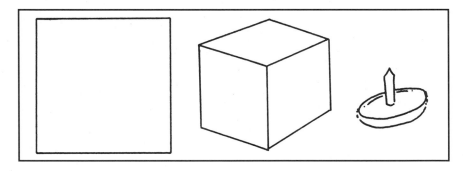

● Make some shadows using the torch and your shape and draw them on another piece of paper.
● Can your friend now make the shadows you have drawn?

Camouflaging fish

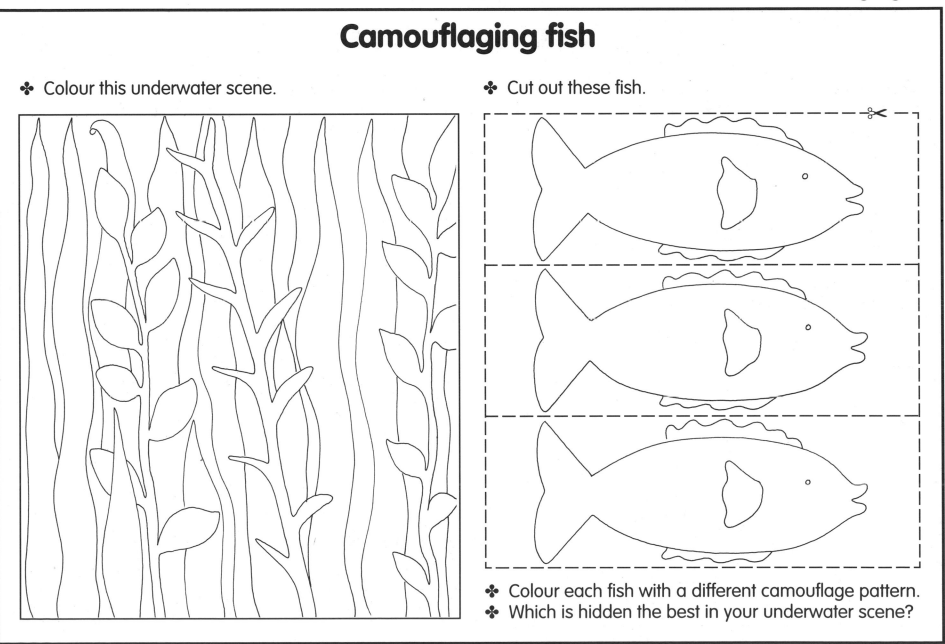

❖ Colour this underwater scene.

❖ Cut out these fish.

❖ Colour each fish with a different camouflage pattern.
❖ Which is hidden the best in your underwater scene?

Camouflaged moths

Name _____

Camouflaged moths

The moths opposite need to hide on this tree trunk.

✤ Colour all these pictures using the same colours.

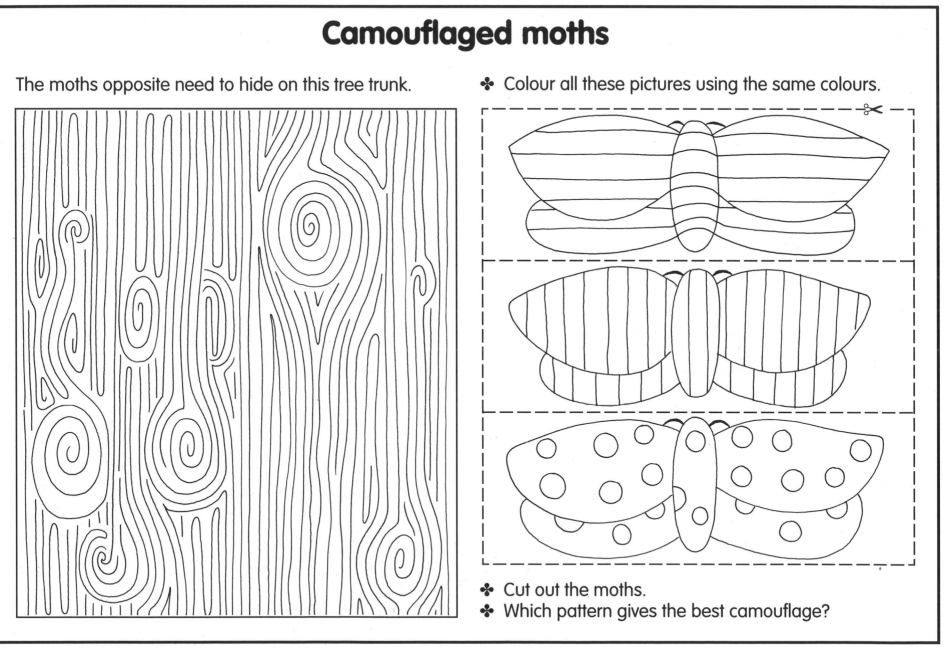

✤ Cut out the moths.
✤ Which pattern gives the best camouflage?

Rainbow wheel

White light can be split up into the colours of the rainbow:

> violet   indigo   blue   green
> yellow   orange   red

♣ Try to mix these colours again by making a **rainbow spinner**.

You will need: a length of dowel, a wooden wheel, a pencil sharpener, a cardboard disc, felt-tipped pens.

1 Sharpen the end of the wooden dowel.

2 Fix this into a wooden wheel to make a spinner.

3 Cut out a cardboard disc to sit on top of the spinner.

Use felt-tipped pens and try different patterns.

4 Colour the disc with the colours of the rainbow.

You could glue on coloured paper from magazines.

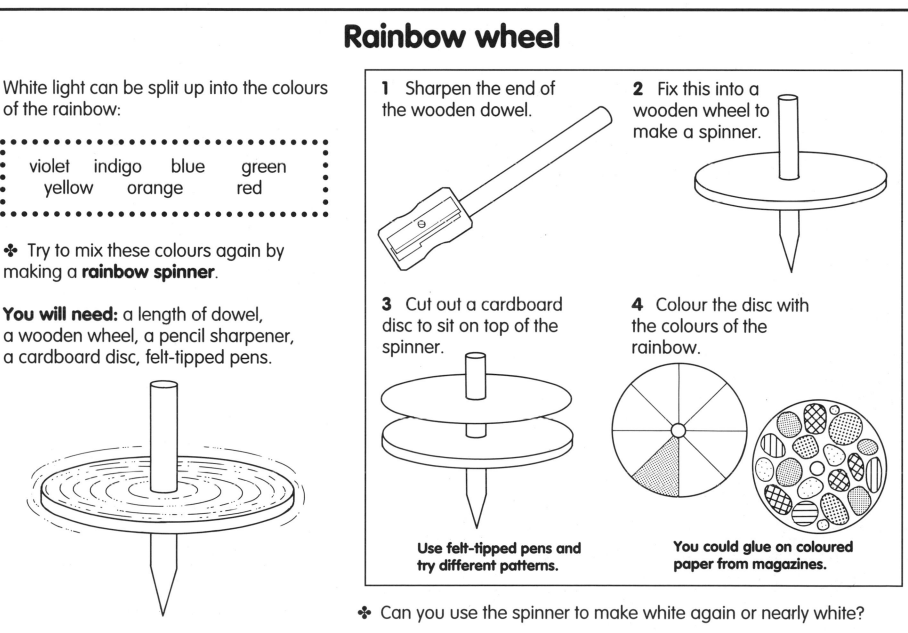

♣ Can you use the spinner to make white again or nearly white?

Reflections

You will need: a small rectangle of perspex or glass to act as a mirror.

❧ Stand the 'mirror' along the line in each box below.
❧ Look at the reflection of each shape.
❧ What shape do you see? Draw it behind the mirror.
❧ Make up some more shapes of your own.

1   mirror

2   mirror

3   mirror

4   mirror

5   mirror

6   mirror   Draw your own shape here.

Spots before your eyes

♣ Stare at the black spot while you count to 50. Then look in the white square.

♣ What do you see?

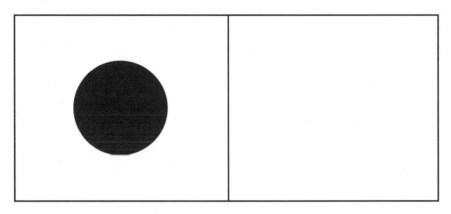

♣ Stare at the white star while you count to 50. Then look in the white square.

♣ What do you see?

♣ Now investigate one of these questions:

• Does using your left eye, your right eye or both eyes give the same result?

• Does the image in the white square stay for longer if you stare for longer?

• What is the effect of using different coloured spots or shapes?

♣ Record the results of your investigation carefully for others to see.

♣ Can you think of more questions to ask?

Name _____

Bending light

We see things clearly when light is reflected off them straight into our eyes. If the reflected light is made to turn corners, then things seem to change shape.

✤ Investigate these changing shapes using a plastic drink bottle filled with water.

• Make a simple shape to look at, such as this:

• Look at the shape through the bottle.

• Record all the different images which you see through the bottle. (The shape may turn round!)

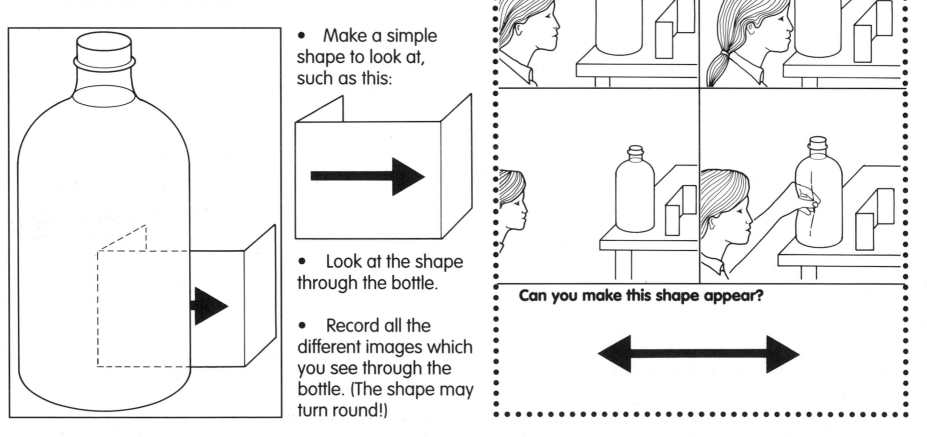

Try these ideas to start you off.

Can you make this shape appear?

Fun with two mirrors

You will need: two small flat mirrors, sticky tape, a small object such as a marble.

♣ Tape the two mirrors together like this:

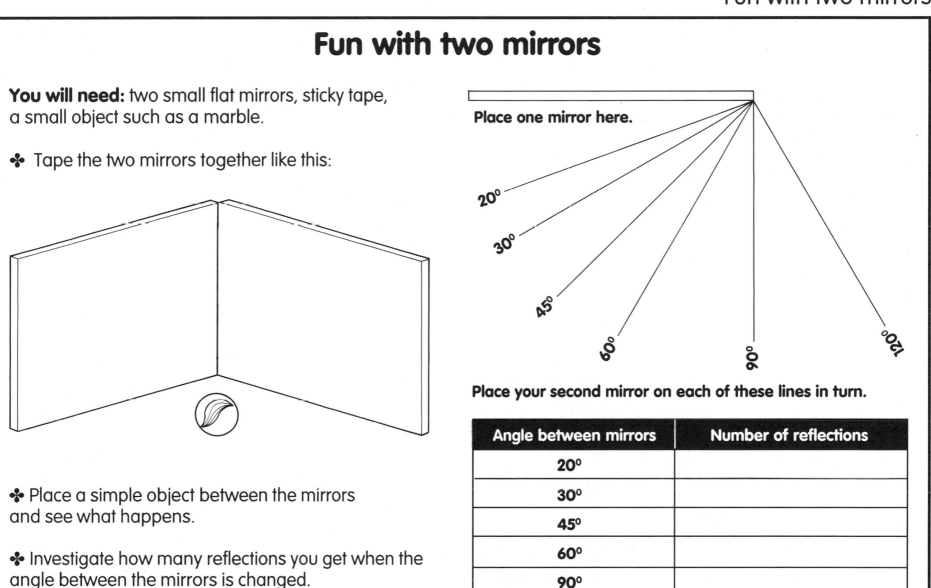

Place one mirror here.

20°

30°

45°

60°

90°

120°

Place your second mirror on each of these lines in turn.

♣ Place a simple object between the mirrors and see what happens.

♣ Investigate how many reflections you get when the angle between the mirrors is changed.

♣ Record your results in the table opposite.

Angle between mirrors	Number of reflections
20°	
30°	
45°	
60°	
90°	
120°	

Tubular pin-hole camera

♣ Make a pin-hole camera.
You will need: cardboard tubes, black paper, greaseproof or tracing paper, aluminium foil, sticky tape, a needle.

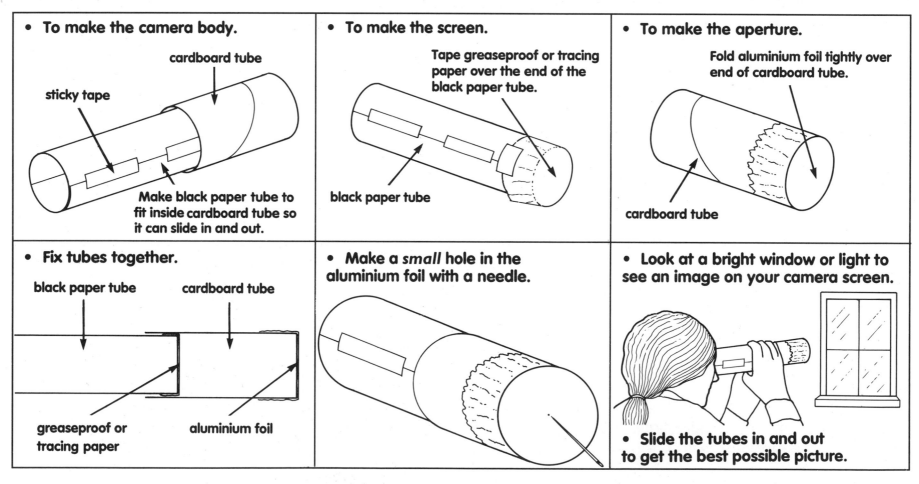

- **To make the camera body.**

cardboard tube

sticky tape

Make black paper tube to fit inside cardboard tube so it can slide in and out.

- **To make the screen.**

Tape greaseproof or tracing paper over the end of the black paper tube.

black paper tube

- **To make the aperture.**

Fold aluminium foil tightly over end of cardboard tube.

cardboard tube

- **Fix tubes together.**

black paper tube   cardboard tube

greaseproof or tracing paper   aluminium foil

- **Make a *small* hole in the aluminium foil with a needle.**

- **Look at a bright window or light to see an image on your camera screen.**

- **Slide the tubes in and out to get the best possible picture.**

♣ Investigate what happens when you make a smaller or larger hole (aperture) in the foil.

Sound makers

All the things on this page make sounds.

❖ Colour in red those things which make sounds by moving air.
❖ Colour in blue those things which make sounds by moving strings.
❖ Colour in green those things which make sounds through something being hit.

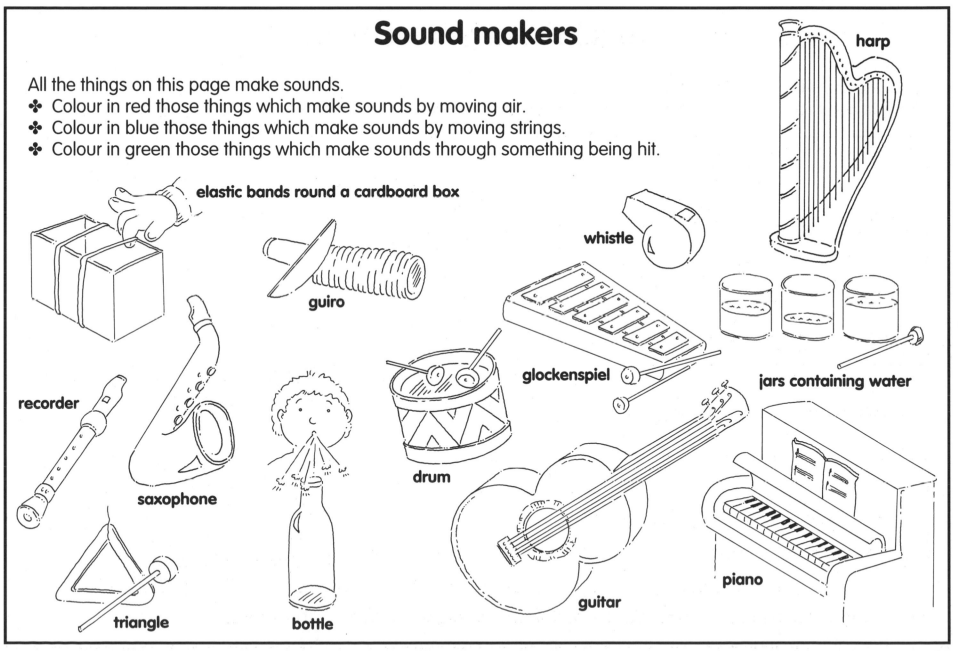

harp

elastic bands round a cardboard box

guiro

whistle

glockenspiel

jars containing water

recorder

saxophone

drum

triangle

bottle

guitar

piano

Which is loudest?

Name _____

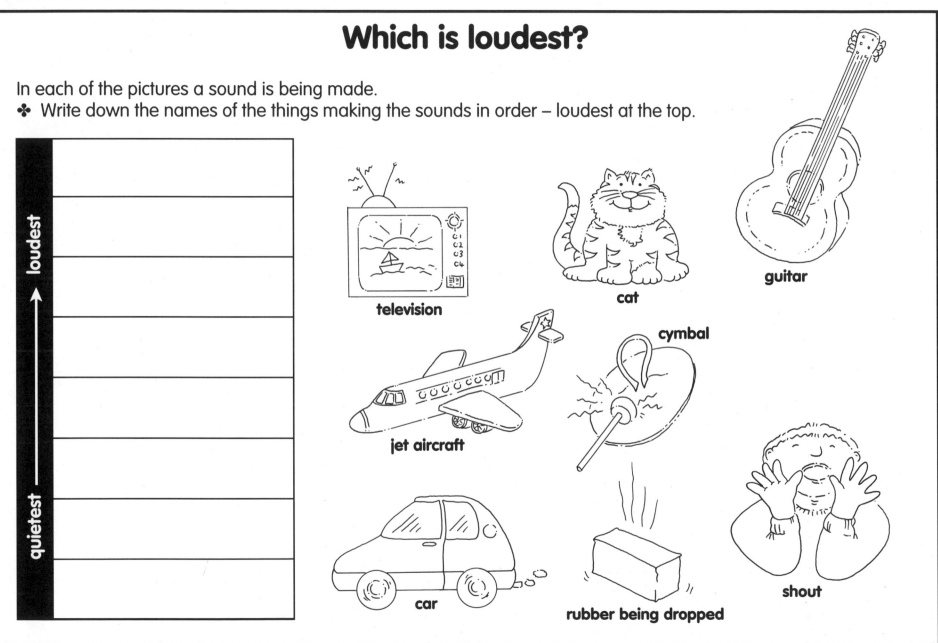

Which is loudest?

In each of the pictures a sound is being made.
♣ Write down the names of the things making the sounds in order – loudest at the top.

loudest

quietest

television

cat

guitar

jet aircraft

cymbal

car

rubber being dropped

shout

96

Mystery sounds

✤ Work with a partner to set up a screen. Use a cardboard box or a table or even a big book.

✤ Make a collection of things that make different sounds. For example:

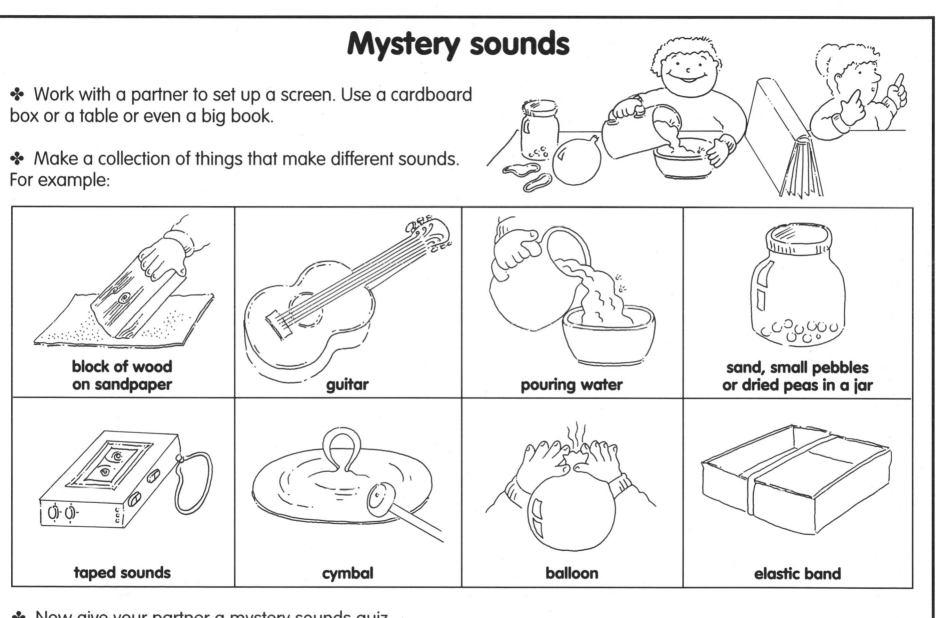

| block of wood on sandpaper | guitar | pouring water | sand, small pebbles or dried peas in a jar |
| taped sounds | cymbal | balloon | elastic band |

✤ Now give your partner a mystery sounds quiz.

Sound survey

Sound survey

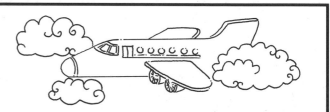

✤ Make a sound survey at different places around school.
Listen very, very carefully. Close your eyes if you want. Then fill in this table.

Time of day	Where I listened	What made the sound?	How far away (close/middle/far)?	Single sound or continuous?	It sounds like ...

✤ Now answer these questions.

- Where did you hear the greatest number of different sounds?
- Which was the loudest sound you heard?
- Which was the quietest sound you heard?
- Does the time of day make a difference to your results?

What makes sounds?

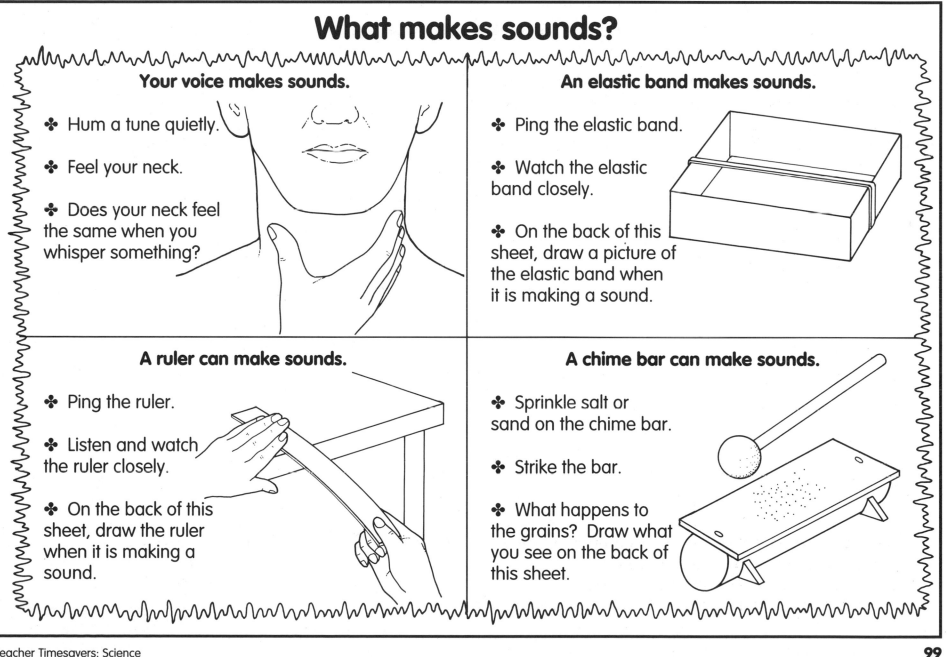

Your voice makes sounds.

✤ Hum a tune quietly.

✤ Feel your neck.

✤ Does your neck feel the same when you whisper something?

An elastic band makes sounds.

✤ Ping the elastic band.

✤ Watch the elastic band closely.

✤ On the back of this sheet, draw a picture of the elastic band when it is making a sound.

A ruler can make sounds.

✤ Ping the ruler.

✤ Listen and watch the ruler closely.

✤ On the back of this sheet, draw the ruler when it is making a sound.

A chime bar can make sounds.

✤ Sprinkle salt or sand on the chime bar.

✤ Strike the bar.

✤ What happens to the grains? Draw what you see on the back of this sheet.

Making sounds louder

Making sounds louder

The picture opposite shows the grooves in a plastic music record. The stylus or needle is made to vibrate in these grooves as the record plays. This makes a very quiet sound which must be made louder.

❖ Investigate how to make quiet sounds louder.

You will need: an old plastic record, a record player, a sewing needle, some small cardboard boxes, sticky tape.

- Tape the needle to the side of one of the boxes.
- Hold the point of the needle in a groove of the record as it is going round on the record player.
- Try different sizes and shapes of box.

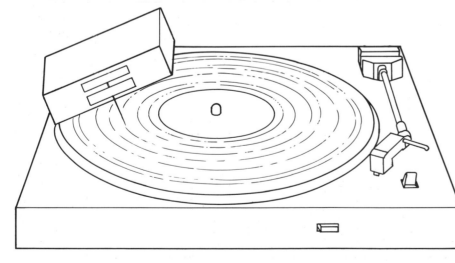

❖ Complete this table for your results.

Shape of box	Length of box (cm)	Volume of sound 1 (quiet) → 10 (loud)

High and low sounds

The highness or lowness of a sound is called its **pitch**.

♣ Quietly hum a low pitched sound and then a high pitched sound.

♣ Find out which of these things make a low pitched sound and which a high pitched sound.

♣ For each of these activities, draw each item in the correct column on the table to show whether it makes a low, medium or high pitched sound.

Sounds made by...	Pitch		
	Low	Medium	High
Three jars with different amounts of water. Tap each in turn with a pencil.			
Ping the elastic band, then move the support outwards and ping again.			
Blow across an empty lemonade bottle. Then try with different amounts of water.			
Ping a ruler at different places on the edge of a table.			

♣ Circle the correct word in this sentence:

High pitched sounds are made when the size of the vibrating thing is small/medium/large.

Name _____

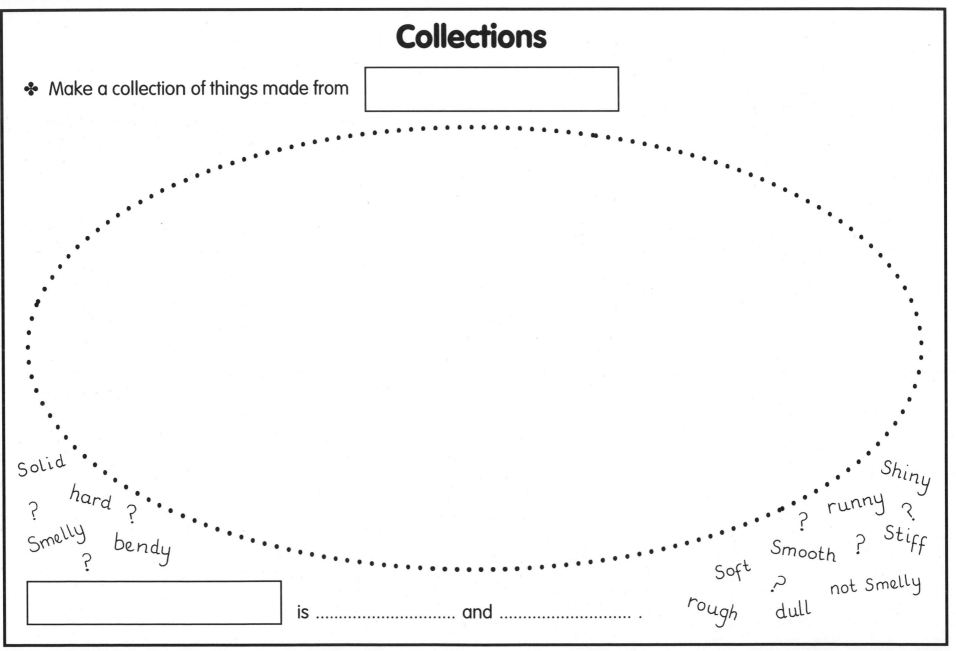

Collections

♣ Make a collection of things made from ☐

Solid
? hard ?
Smelly ? bendy
?

Shiny
? runny ?
Smooth ? Stiff
Soft ?
rough dull not Smelly

☐ is .... and ....

Name _____

In the kitchen

This is Mr Jones' kitchen.

♣ Colour in the things in his kitchen using the key opposite.

metal – blue	**plastic – red**
wood – brown	**textiles – green**
glass – yellow	**china or pottery – orange**

Name _____

In the classroom

This is Davinder's classroom.

✤ Use this colour code opposite to colour in the picture.
✤ Choose another material, colour it in green and add it to the key.

red – plastic   brown – wood
yellow – paper   blue – metal
green – _____

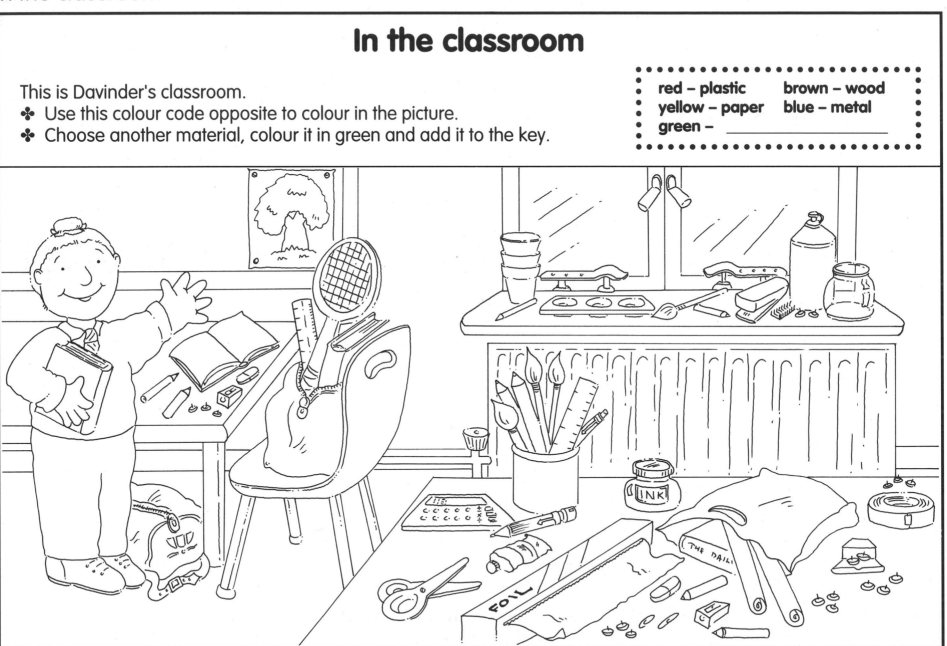

Name _____

Making with materials

✤ Join each of the things below to the material from which it is made. One has already been done for you.

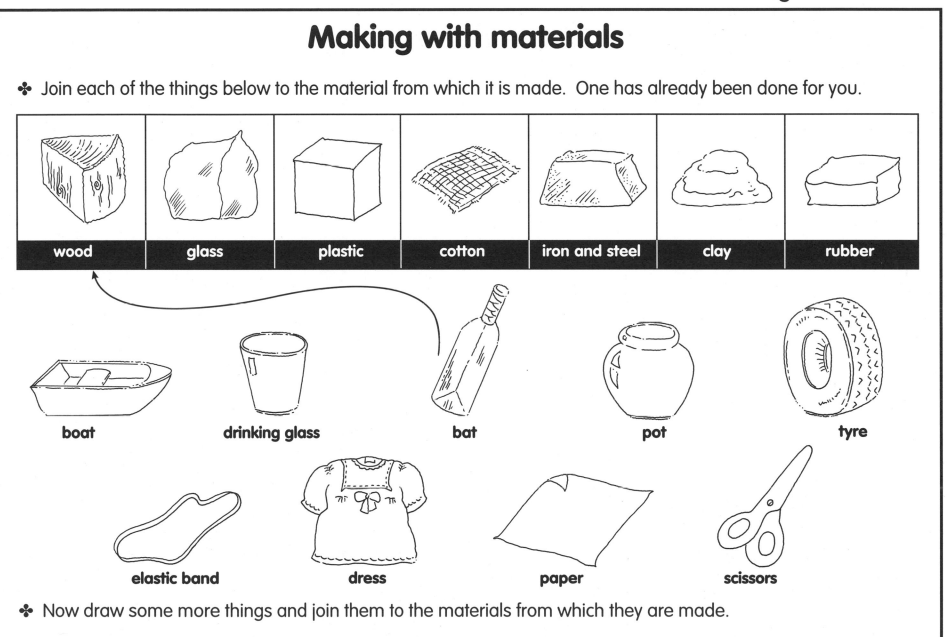

| wood | glass | plastic | cotton | iron and steel | clay | rubber |

boat   drinking glass   bat   pot   tyre

elastic band   dress   paper   scissors

✤ Now draw some more things and join them to the materials from which they are made.

Name _____

Comparing materials: 1

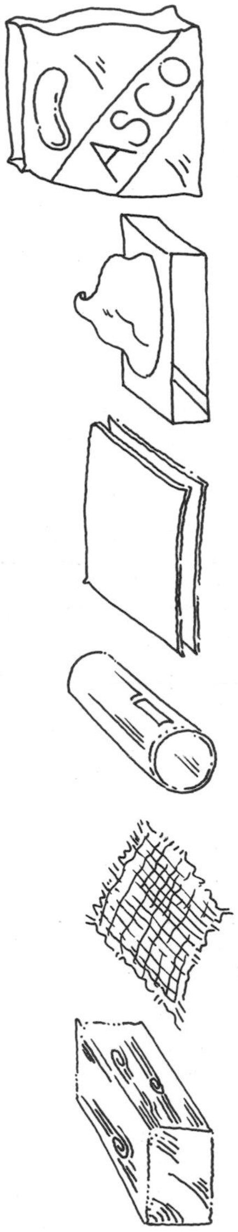

Comparing materials: 1

polythene

tissue

card

metal

cotton

wood

❖ Draw a picture of each material in the correct column.

Feels warm		Soaks up water	
Feels cold		**Waterproof**	

Dull		Stiff	
Shiny		**Bendy**	

Comparing materials: 2

❖ Decide in which column each of these materials belongs.
❖❖ Then draw each material in the correct column.

Plasticine   rubber   foam sponge   glass   iron   hard plastic

Feels warm	Smooth	Not see through	See through

Springy	Not springy	Hard	Soft

Cartoons of properties

Name _____

Cartoons of properties

This cartoon shows a substance and one of its properties.

Property	Substance
sticky	treacle

❖ Decide which substance shows best each of these properties and then fill in the table below.

Property	Substance
elastic	
corrodes (e.g., goes rusty)	
attracted to magnets	
inflammable	
conducts electricity	
light for its size	
vibrates when struck	
brittle	
absorbent	
waterproof	
conducts heat well	
rigid	

❖ Draw some cartoons of your own to show the substances and their properties listed in the table.

Name _____

The wrong substance

Each of these objects has been made with the wrong substance.
❖ Discuss with a friend, why each of these substances should not have been used.

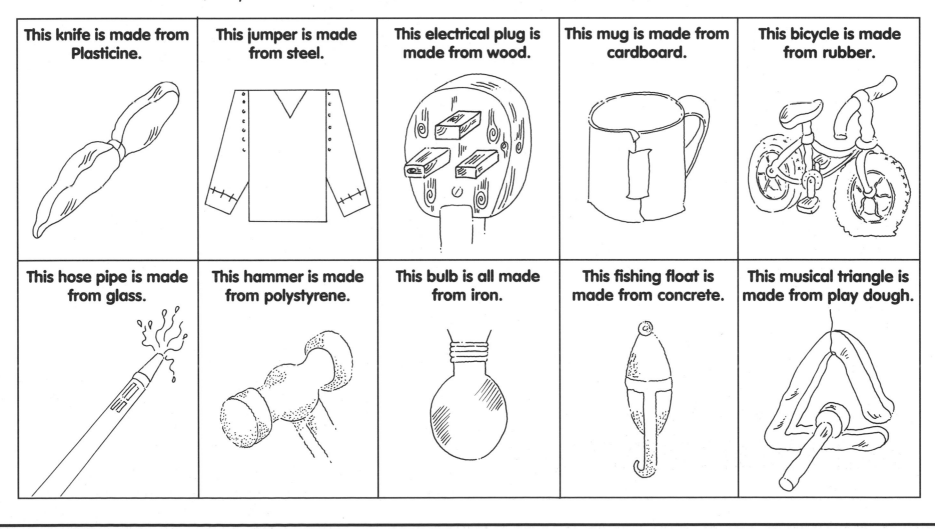

| This knife is made from Plasticine. | This jumper is made from steel. | This electrical plug is made from wood. | This mug is made from cardboard. | This bicycle is made from rubber. |
| This hose pipe is made from glass. | This hammer is made from polystyrene. | This bulb is all made from iron. | This fishing float is made from concrete. | This musical triangle is made from play dough. |

Runny liquids

Runny liquids

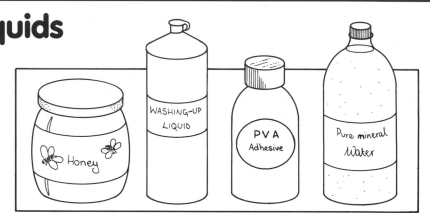

✤ Make a collection of these different liquids: honey, PVA adhesive, washing-up liquid, water.

✤ Which do you think is the least runny and which is the most runny? Try to list them in order of runniness (viscosity).

_____

_____

✤ Now make up a test to see if your prediction was correct.

one teaspoon of the liquid

start line

finish line

✤ You may like to consider:
• How much slope you will use?
• How far the liquid must travel?
• If you will use the same surface each time?

✤ Record your results on this table.

Liquid	Time to travel [ ] cm

✤ Did you put your liquids in the correct order?

Star constellations

Constellations are patterns of stars which suggest a picture.
* Look at the two constellations below.
* Draw the picture around each of them that they suggest to you.

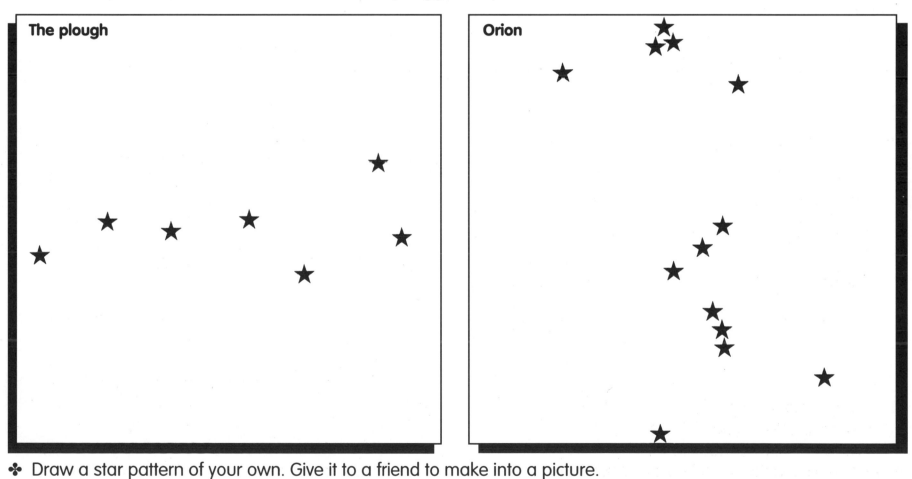

The plough

Orion

* Draw a star pattern of your own. Give it to a friend to make into a picture.

Seasonal shadows

Seasonal shadows

The pictures below show shadows at different times in the day.
* Cut out each set of pictures and stick them on to another
piece of paper in the correct order.
* Write the approximate time of day in the box on each picture.

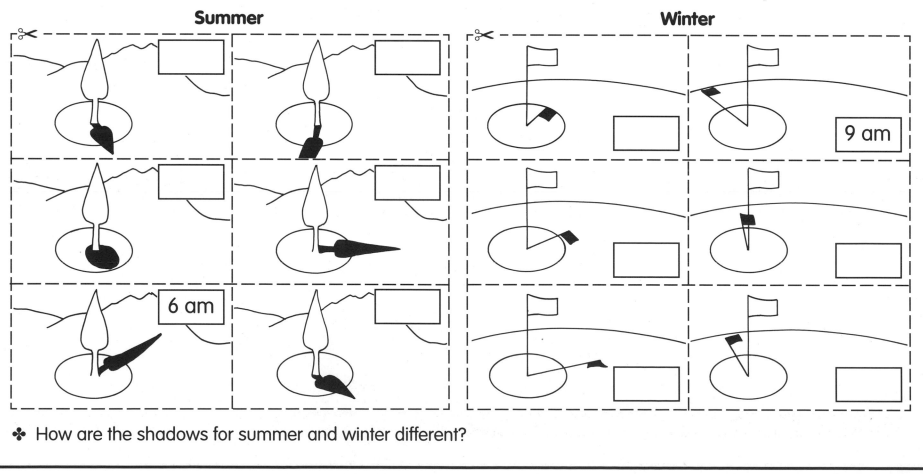

Summer

Winter

9 am

6 am

* How are the shadows for summer and winter different?

How big is everything?

❖ Cut out the four pictures below and stick them on to another piece of paper in order of size.
❖ Write **largest** and **smallest** under the correct pictures.

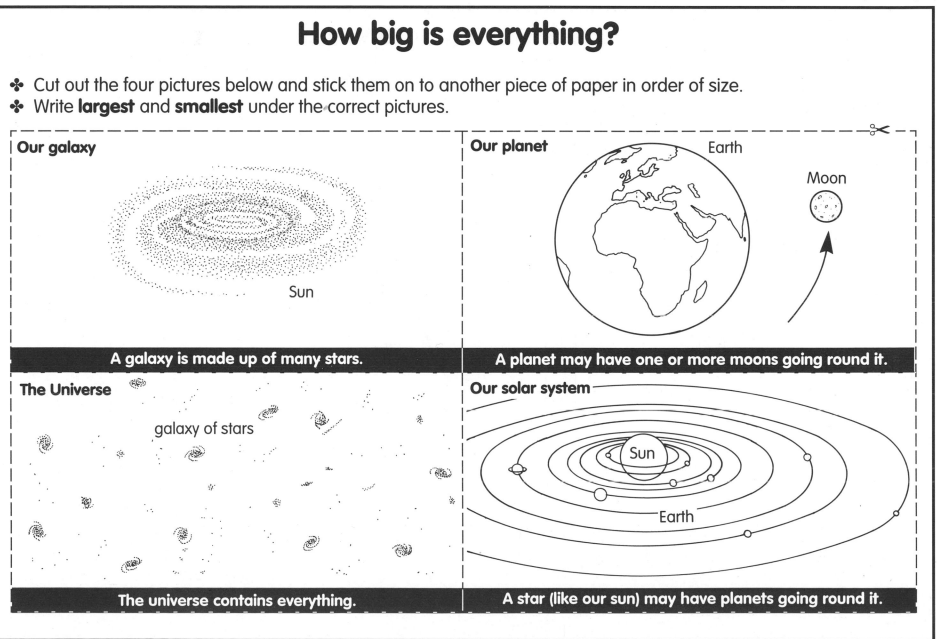

Our galaxy

Sun

A galaxy is made up of many stars.

Our planet   Earth

Moon

A planet may have one or more moons going round it.

The Universe

galaxy of stars

The universe contains everything.

Our solar system

Sun

Earth

A star (like our sun) may have planets going round it.

The inner solar system

The inner solar system

You will need : a piece of paper at least 30cm x 30cm, adhesive, paper fasteners, a pair of compasses.

♣ Prepare a coloured background sheet of paper like this:

♣ Cut out the sun and planets below and fix them to the background like this:

Use a paper fastener.

14cm

8cm   5cm

Stick these on.

Sun

♣ Move your model to show:
- one day passing;
- one month passing;
- a full moon;
- a new moon;
- one year passing.

♣ How many rotations of the moon are there in one year?

Moon

Earth

Sun

Venus

Mercury

Our solar system

The planets in our solar system are:

Earth   **Jupiter**   **Mars**   **Mercury**   **Neptune**
    Pluto   **Saturn**   **Uranus**   **Venus**

The planets are shown drawn to the same scale for their size (but not the correct distance apart) and in the correct order from the Sun.

❖   Use reference books to find out which planet is which and label them.

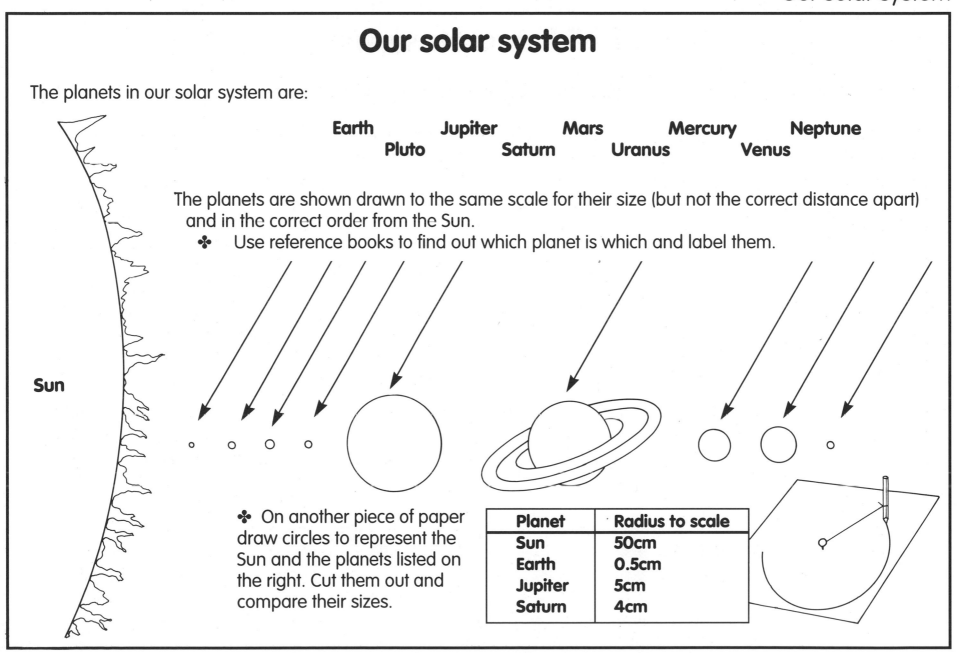

Sun

❖ On another piece of paper draw circles to represent the Sun and the planets listed on the right. Cut them out and compare their sizes.

Planet	Radius to scale
Sun	50cm
Earth	0.5cm
Jupiter	5cm
Saturn	4cm

Name _____

Solids and shadows

Solids and shadows

We can only see things if they give out light or if they reflect light from somewhere else.

❖ Investigate light and shadow patterns on solid shapes.
- Find some three-dimensional shapes, like these:

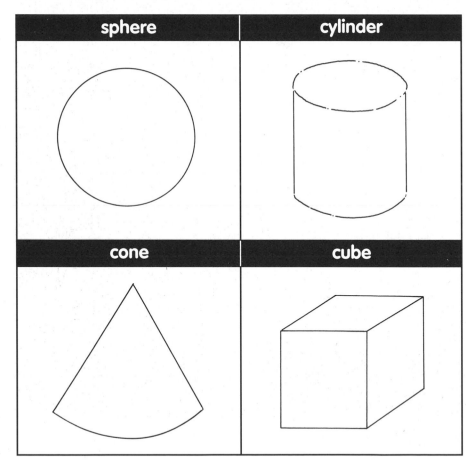

sphere	cylinder
cone	cube

- Put the shapes in a darkened place and shine a torch on them from the side.

- On the back of this sheet, draw the parts of each shape which are in the light.

Mysteries in the dark

The pictures below show some everyday objects in a dark room.
The light shining on them comes from one side only.

♣ Draw what you think each object would look like in full light.

Moon models

Name _____

Moon models

The picture below shows Julie standing in the middle of a darkened room. She is holding a ball in a strong light. We can see her from above. Julie's head is like the Earth and the ball is like the moon. The light acts like the Sun.

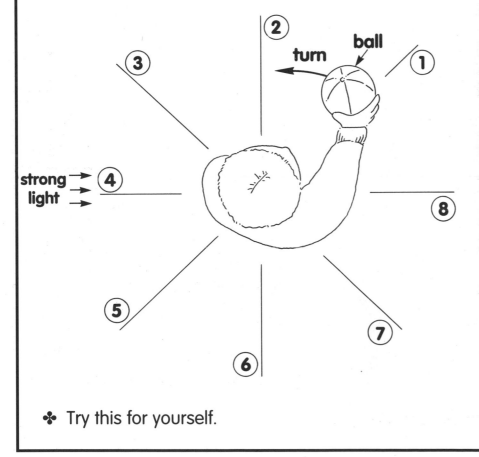

✤ Try this for yourself.

This is how Julie sees the light falling on the ball in different positions as she turns round.

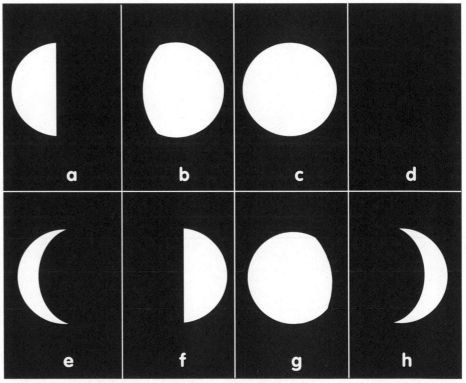

✤ Which picture (a–h) goes with which position (1–8)?

✤ Find out the names of the phases of the moon that match the pictures a–h.

Spinning on its axis

♣ Look at the pictures below. They show three different planets. Planet Earth is real, the others are imaginary. Each planet spins round once every 24 hours on its (imaginary) axis.

Planet Earth	Planet Vertigo	Planet Horisonto

Planet Earth: axis, Edith, DARK, LIGHT, Edward, Sunlight

Planet Vertigo: axis, Vera, Vernon, Sunlight

Planet Horisonto: Hannah, Harry, axis, Sunlight

♣ Write about the length of day and night for each of the six people shown.

Space and time

Name _____

Space and time

12 hours

Each of the pictures and labels below show a time or the passing of time.

One week

♣ Match each label to the correct picture.

Summer in Britain

Earth spins round once.

Earth

Earth goes once round the Sun.

Earth

Sun

Sun's rays

Earth

Winter in Britain

One month

One day

Moon goes once round the Earth.

Moon

Earth

Moon goes a quarter of the way round the Earth.

Moon

Earth

Sun's rays

Earth

One year

Earth spins half way round.

Earth

Weather pictures

Weather forecasters use pictures to show us the kinds of weather we will have each day.

✤ Cut out the weather symbols below and stick the correct symbol on the weather record each day.

Monday	Tuesday	Wednesday	Thursday	Friday

Cloudy

Cloudy with rain

Sunny

Windy

Snow

Disappearing puddles

Disappearing puddles

Water moves slowly into the surrounding air to become water vapour.
This is called **evaporation**.

❖ Investigate evaporation in the playground and/or the classroom by carrying out these tasks.

In the playground
You will need: a bucket of water, chalk, camera or paper and pencil.

• Make a puddle in the playground in the morning with the bucket of water.

• Draw round it in chalk every hour until the end of the day.

• Take a photograph or make a drawing of the pattern you have made.

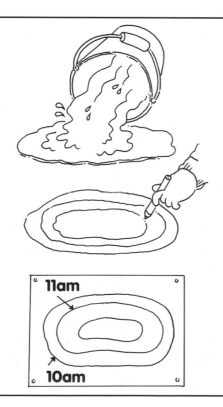

In the classroom
You will need: a saucer of water, a chinagraph pencil and/or waterproof marker pen, camera or paper and pencil.

• Make a 'puddle' in a saucer.

• Draw round the edge of the water every hour with a chinagraph pencil or waterproof marker pen.

• Take a photograph or make a drawing of the pattern you have made.

Tilt the saucer a little.

How much time?

❖ Read the following list of activities:
- Write your name.
- Count to 100.
- Draw a circle.
- Write the alphabet.
- Copy this sentence carefully.

❖ Write down how long you think each activity would take.

❖ Ask a friend to time you doing each activity. Use a stop-watch or stop-clock and record your results in the table opposite.

❖ Now write the list of activities in order of the actual time it takes to do them.

Activity	Time taken to do each activity	
	Guess	Actual time
Write your name.		
Count to 100.		
Draw a circle.		
Write the alphabet.		
Copy this sentence carefully.		

Name _____

Time of day

Time of day

✤ Use this table to record what you do at different times today.
You could predict what you may be doing later today or you could just record things as they happen.

Today is	(day)	(date)

Time of day	What I did today
Before 7.00	
7.00	
7.15	
7.30	
7.45	
8.00	
8.15	
8.30	
8.45	
9.00	
9.15	
9.30	
9.45	
10.00	
10.15	
10.30	
10.45	
11.00	
11.15	
11.30	
11.45	
12.00	
12.15	
12.30	
12.45	
1.00	
1.15	
1.30	
1.45	
2.00	
2.15	
2.30	
2.45	
3.00	
3.15	
3.30	
3.45	
4.00	
4.15	
4.30	
4.45	
5.00	
5.15	
5.30	
5.45	
6.00	
After 6.00	

Teacher Timesavers: Science

Name _____

Weather forecasts

Is the weather forecast always right?

❖ Use this table to write down the weather forecast for today. You could read a newspaper, watch the television, listen to the radio or use the telephone. (Ask an adult's permission before using the telephone.) Then fill in what really happens in your area.

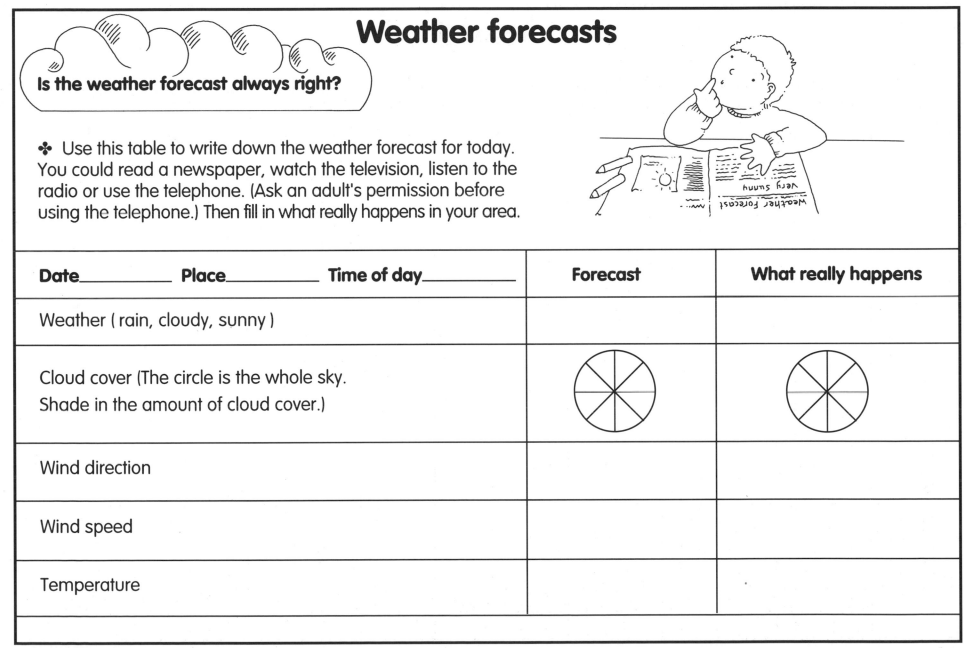

Date_____ Place_____ Time of day_____	Forecast	What really happens
Weather (rain, cloudy, sunny)		
Cloud cover (The circle is the whole sky. Shade in the amount of cloud cover.)		
Wind direction		
Wind speed		
Temperature		

Name _____

Rainfall

Class 2Y collected the rainwater in their rain-gauge each day for a week in January.
It was a very rainy week!

❧ Complete this table to show their results.

Day	Volume of water (millilitres)
3 January	
4 January	
5 January	
6 January	
7 January	
8 January	
9 January	

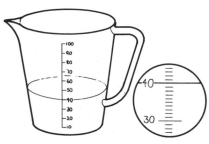

Monday 3 January

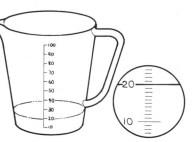

Tuesday 4 January

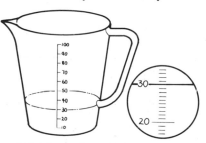

Wednesday 5 January

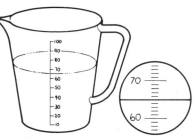

Thursday 6 January

Friday 7 January

Saturday 8 January

Sunday 9 January

❧ Draw a block graph on the back of this sheet to show these results.

❧ Which day was the wettest?

❧ Predict the rainfall for Monday 10 January.

Sundial

Sundial

❖ Make a simple sundial and place it on a sheet of paper. Here are some suggestions:

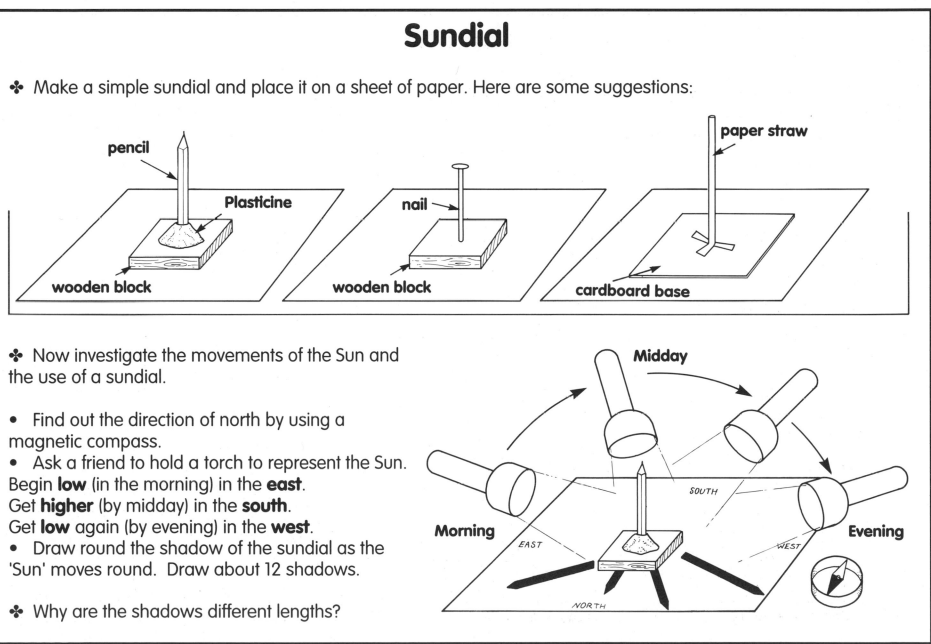

❖ Now investigate the movements of the Sun and the use of a sundial.

• Find out the direction of north by using a magnetic compass.
• Ask a friend to hold a torch to represent the Sun.
Begin **low** (in the morning) in the **east**.
Get **higher** (by midday) in the **south**.
Get **low** again (by evening) in the **west**.
• Draw round the shadow of the sundial as the 'Sun' moves round. Draw about 12 shadows.

❖ Why are the shadows different lengths?

Cycles model

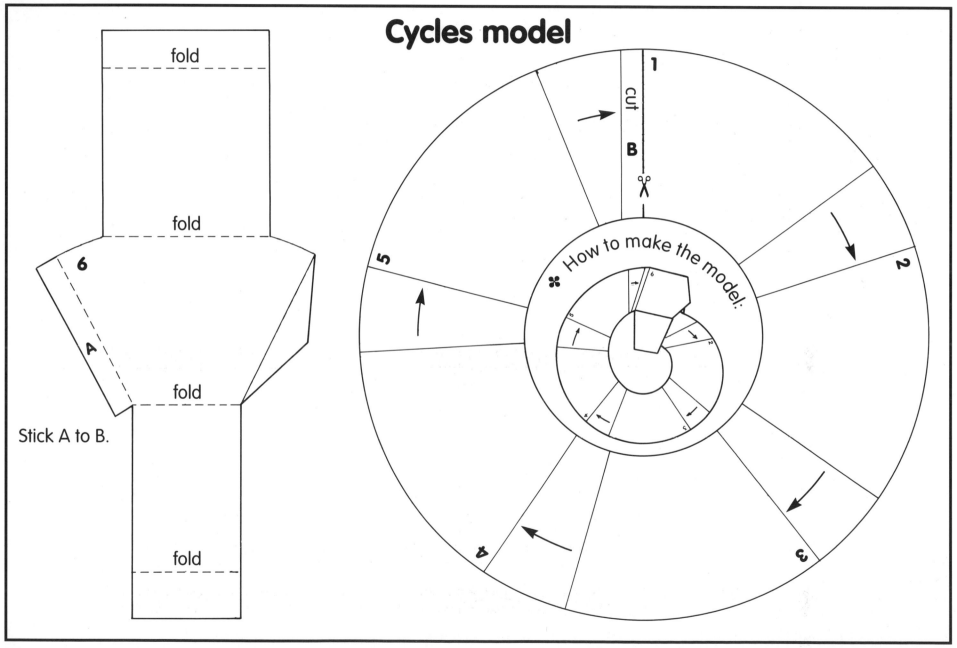

Cycles model

fold

fold

6

A

fold

Stick A to B.

fold

cut

B

1

2

3

4

5

How to make the model:

Cycles: people

These pictures show some of the stages in the life of a person.
- ✤ Cut them out and put them in order.
- ✤ Stick them on to the 'Cycles model' to show the human life cycle.

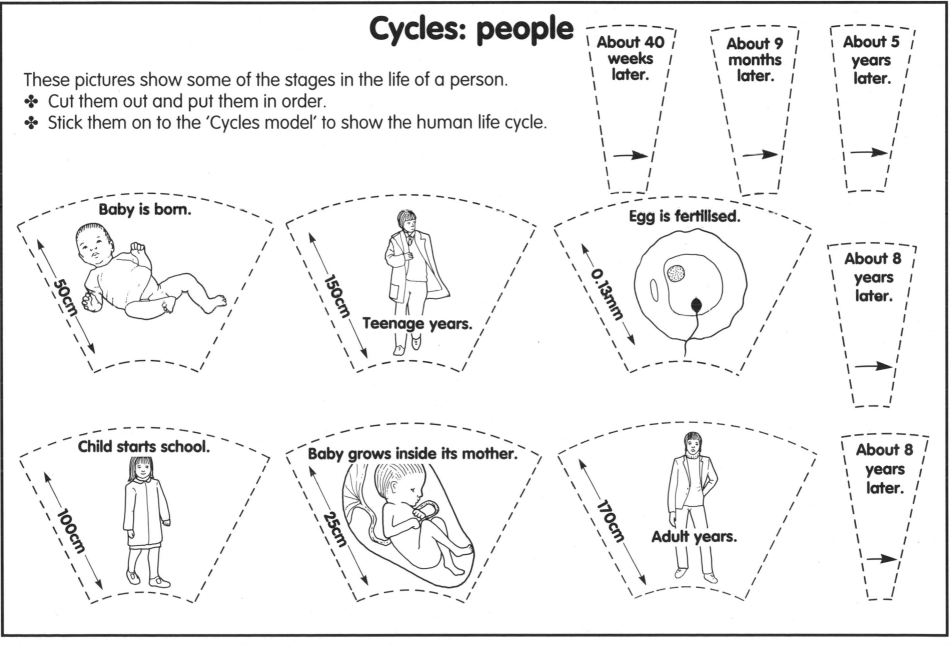

About 40 weeks later.

About 9 months later.

About 5 years later.

Baby is born.

50cm

Teenage years.

150cm

Egg is fertilised.

0.13mm

About 8 years later.

Child starts school.

100cm

Baby grows inside its mother.

25cm

Adult years.

170cm

About 8 years later.

Cycles: housefly

❖ Look at these pictures of the different stages in the life of a housefly.

❖ Cut them out and put them in order.

❖ Stick them on to the 'Cycles model' to show the life cycle of the housefly.

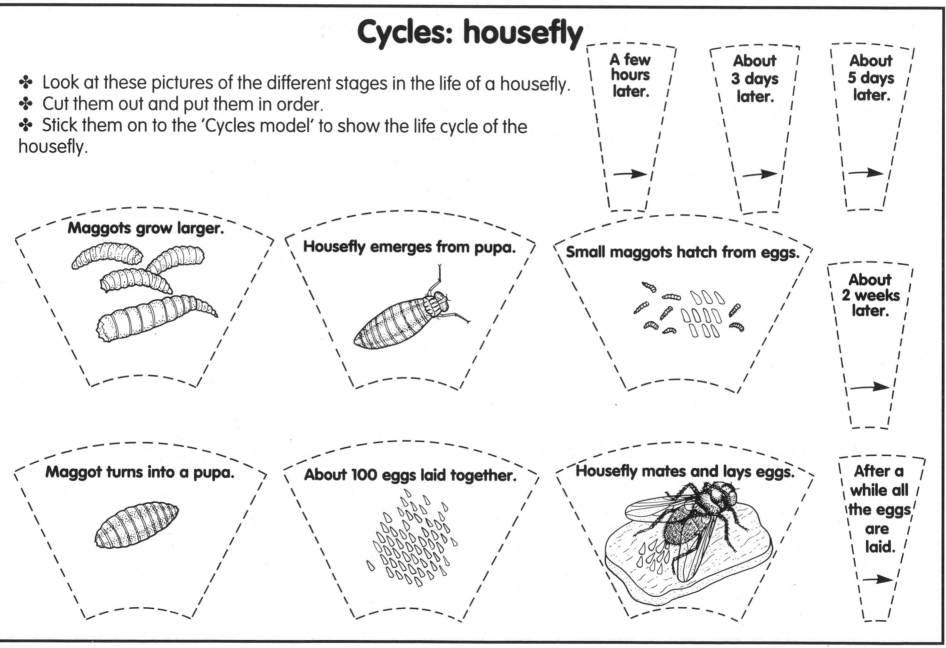

A few hours later.

About 3 days later.

About 5 days later.

Maggots grow larger.

Housefly emerges from pupa.

Small maggots hatch from eggs.

About 2 weeks later.

Maggot turns into a pupa.

About 100 eggs laid together.

Housefly mates and lays eggs.

After a while all the eggs are laid.

Cycles: buttercup plant

These pictures show the stages in the life of a flowering plant – the buttercup.

❖ Cut them out and put them in order.

❖ Stick them on to the 'Cycles model' to show the life cycle of the buttercup.

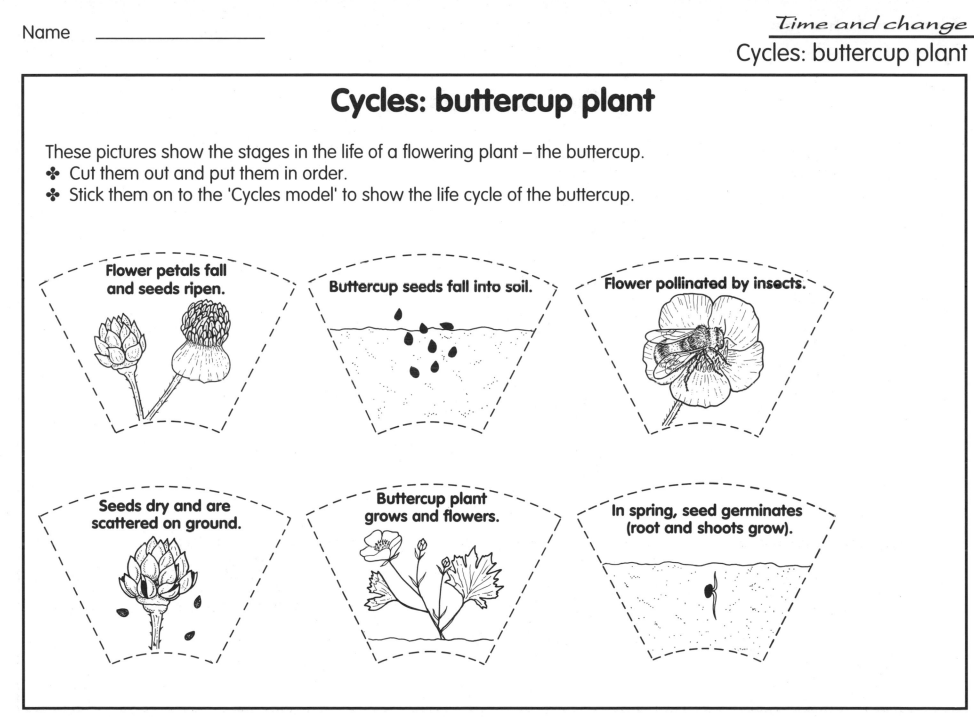

Flower petals fall and seeds ripen.

Buttercup seeds fall into soil.

Flower pollinated by insects.

Seeds dry and are scattered on ground.

Buttercup plant grows and flowers.

In spring, seed germinates (root and shoots grow).

Cycles: the water cycle.

Cycles: the water cycle

All the water we use comes back to us as rain. These pictures show what happens to the water before we can use it again.

♣ Cut out the pictures and put them in order.

♣ Stick them on to the 'Cycles model' to show the water cycle.

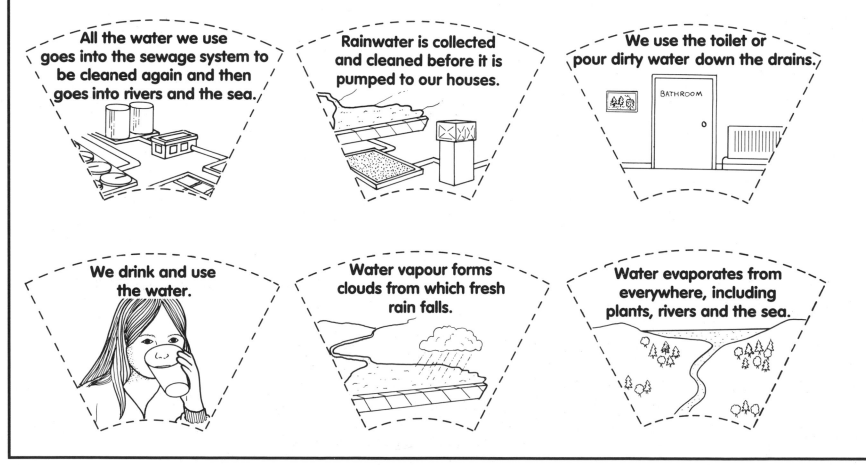

All the water we use goes into the sewage system to be cleaned again and then goes into rivers and the sea.

Rainwater is collected and cleaned before it is pumped to our houses.

We use the toilet or pour dirty water down the drains.

BATHROOM

We drink and use the water.

Water vapour forms clouds from which fresh rain falls.

Water evaporates from everywhere, including plants, rivers and the sea.

Name _____

Glider

------- fold

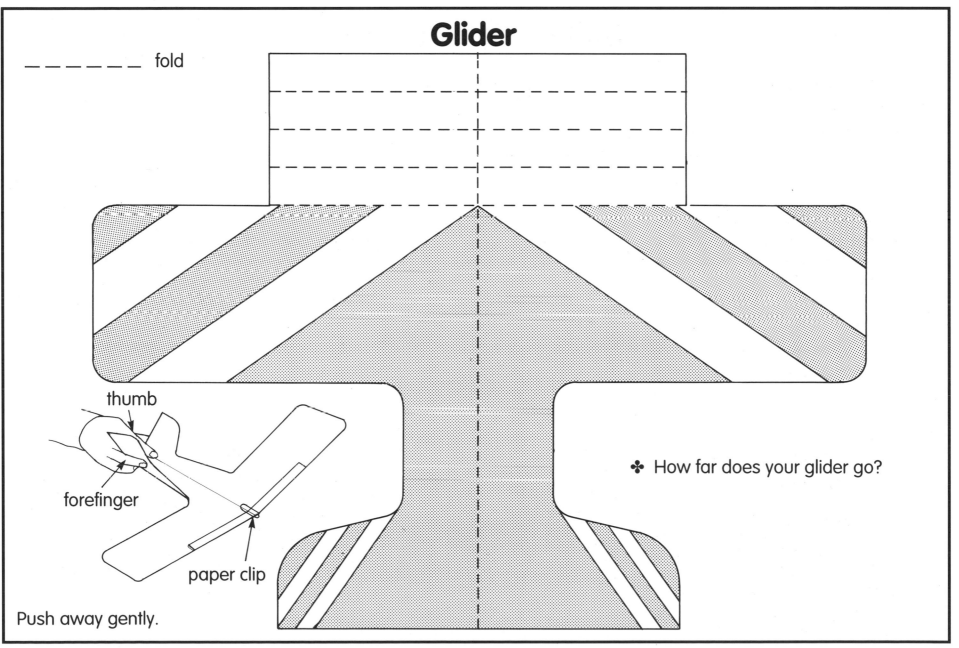

thumb

forefinger

paper clip

❖ How far does your glider go?

Push away gently.

Name _____

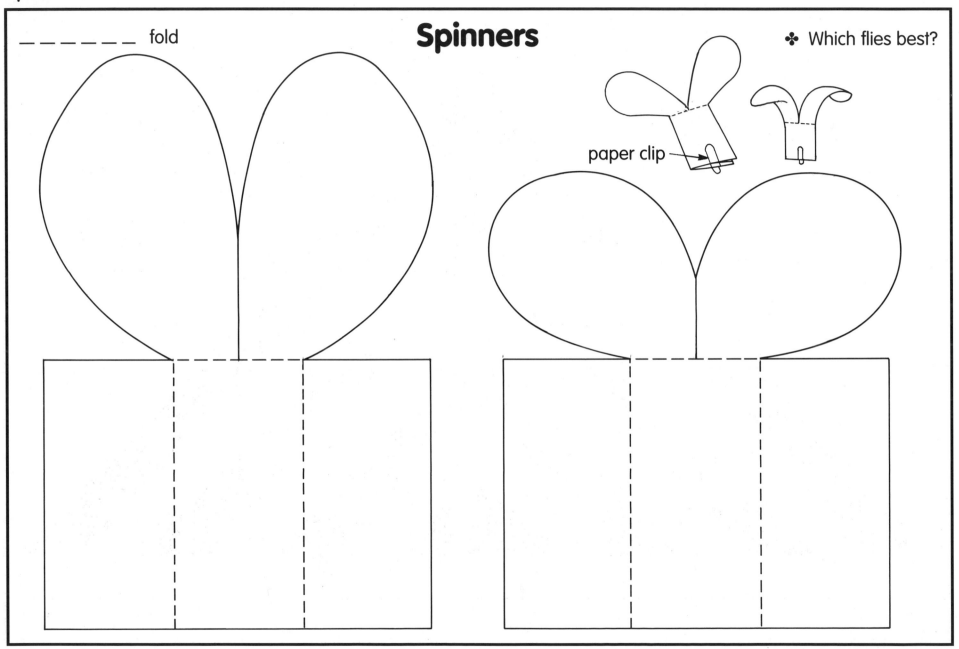

Spinners

- - - - - - - - fold

❖ Which flies best?

paper clip →

Tube glider

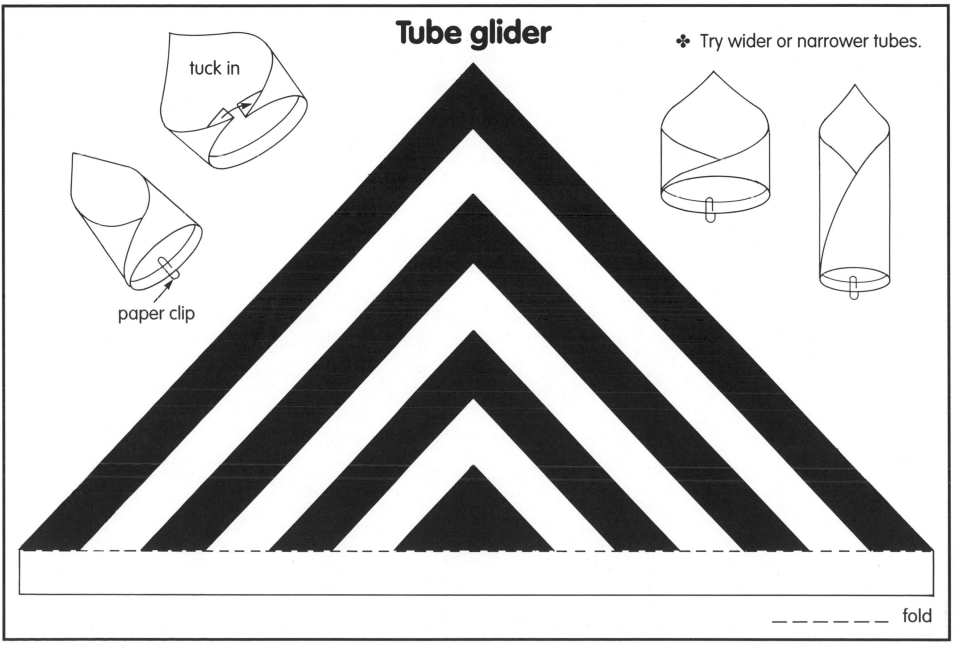

tuck in

paper clip

❖ Try wider or narrower tubes.

fold

Parachute

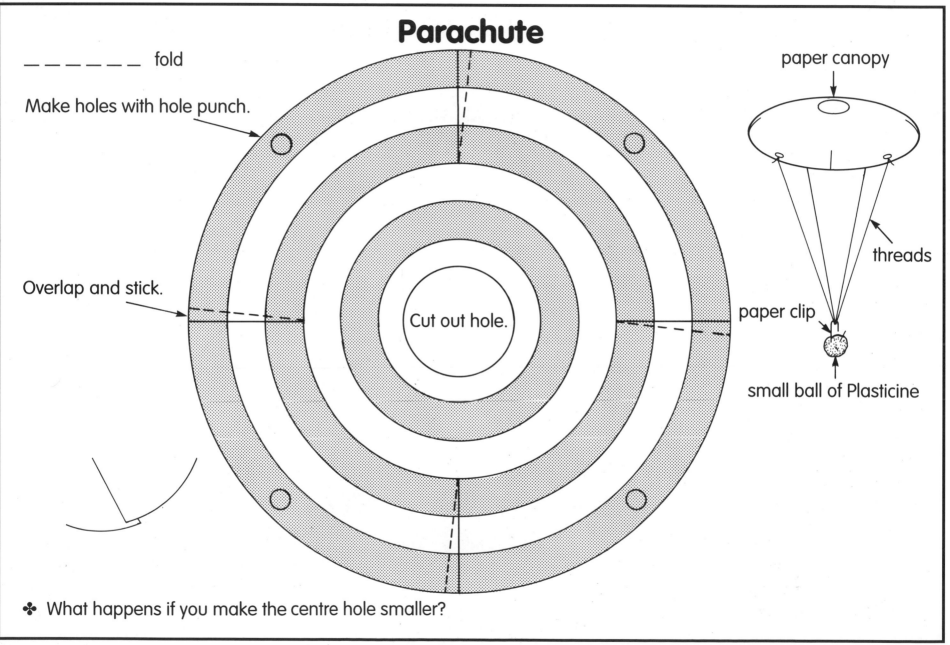

Parachute

— — — — — — — fold

Make holes with hole punch.

Overlap and stick.

Cut out hole.

paper canopy

threads

paper clip

small ball of Plasticine

❖ What happens if you make the centre hole smaller?

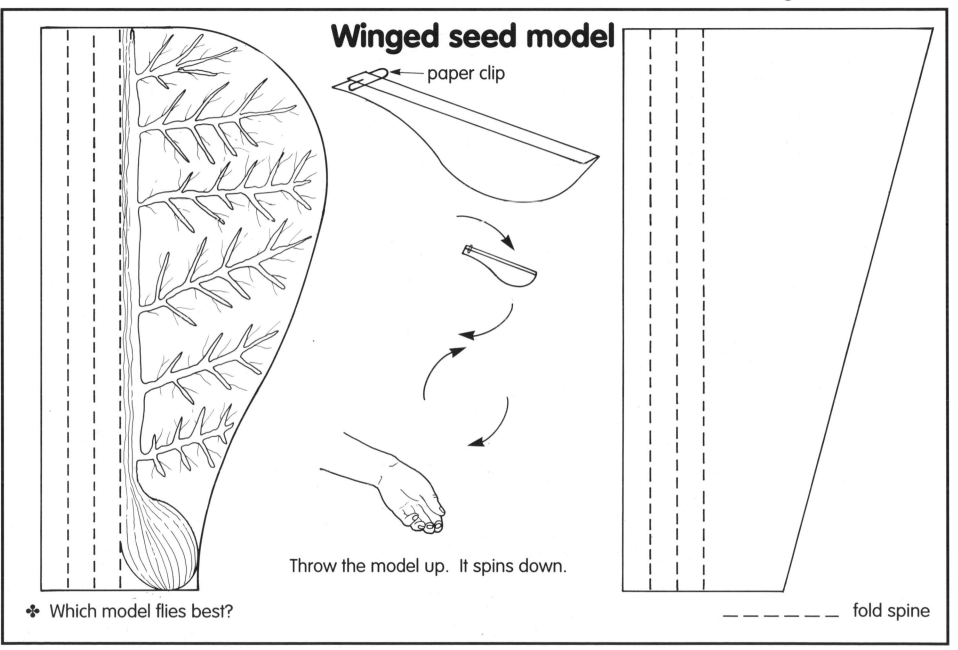

Winged seed model

paper clip

Throw the model up. It spins down.

fold spine

❖ Which model flies best?

Circumferences

Circumferences

You can measure the circumference of something by using a paper strip or string, like this:

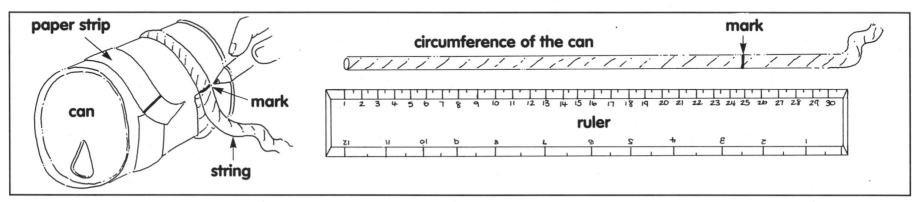

❖ Measure the circumference of these parts of your body. Guess first.

	My guess (cm)	Actual measurement (cm)
head		
neck		
waist		
wrist		
thumb		
little finger		
knee		
ankle		

138

Name _____

Match the volume

❖ Draw a line to join each container to its volume.

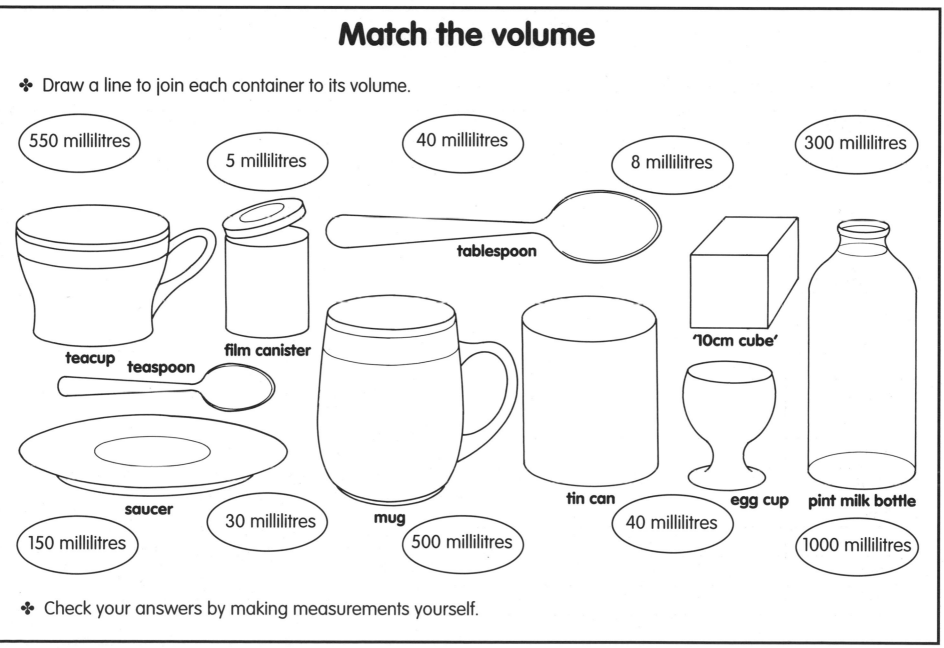

550 millilitres

5 millilitres

40 millilitres

8 millilitres

300 millilitres

tablespoon

teacup

teaspoon

film canister

'10cm cube'

saucer

mug

tin can

egg cup

pint milk bottle

150 millilitres

30 millilitres

500 millilitres

40 millilitres

1000 millilitres

❖ Check your answers by making measurements yourself.

Matching mass

Matching mass

✤ Draw a line to join each object to its mass.

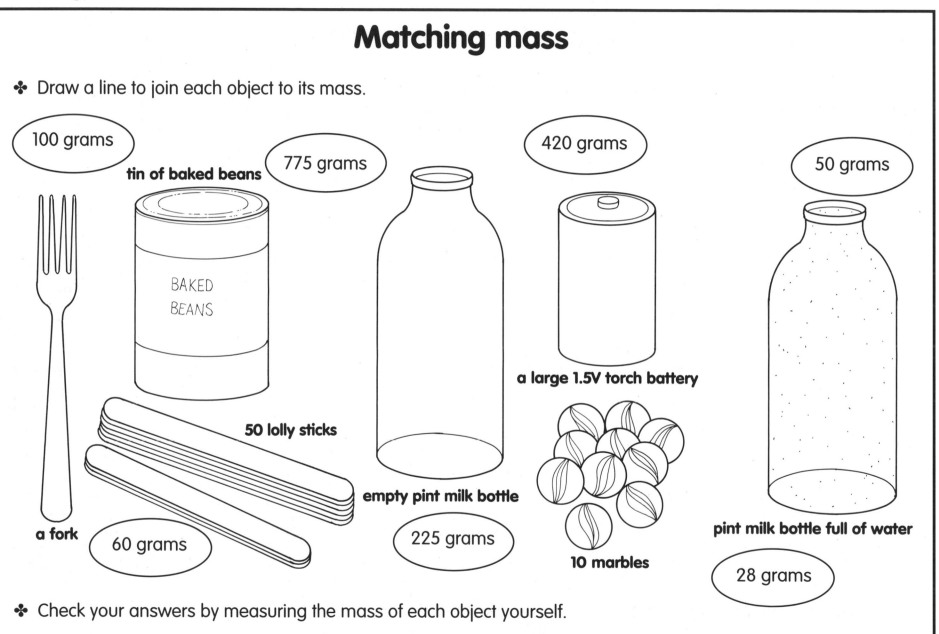

100 grams

775 grams

420 grams

50 grams

tin of baked beans

BAKED BEANS

a large 1.5V torch battery

50 lolly sticks

empty pint milk bottle

pint milk bottle full of water

a fork

60 grams

225 grams

10 marbles

28 grams

✤ Check your answers by measuring the mass of each object yourself.

Match the temperature

✤ Draw a line to join each picture to the correct temperature.
Note: °C means degrees Celsius.

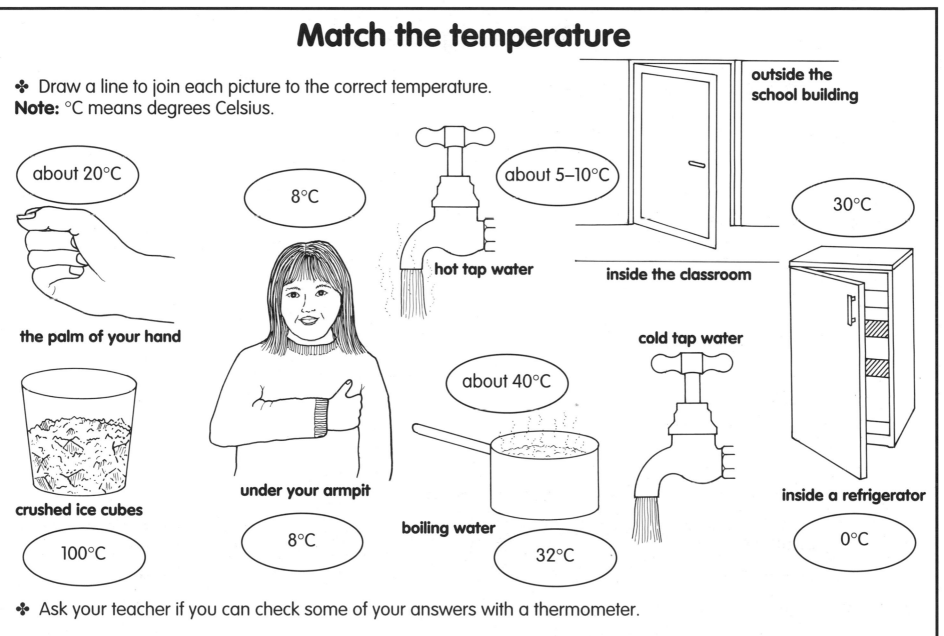

about 20°C

8°C

about 5–10°C

30°C

hot tap water

outside the school building

inside the classroom

the palm of your hand

cold tap water

about 40°C

crushed ice cubes

under your armpit

boiling water

inside a refrigerator

100°C

8°C

32°C

0°C

✤ Ask your teacher if you can check some of your answers with a thermometer.

Shade detective

Shade detective

Light colours reflect more light than darker colours. You can compare the lightness or darkness of a colour.

You will need: a black and white photograph from an old newspaper.
❖ Cut out six pieces from the photograph which are black or have different shades of grey on them.
❖ Stick them in order, on another sheet of paper, like this:

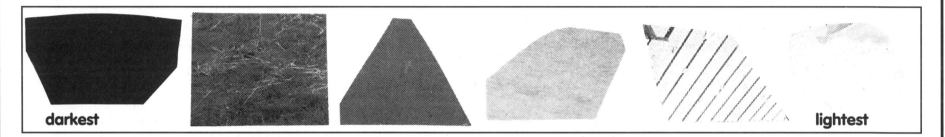

darkest   lightest

You will need: a picture from a colour magazine
❖ Cut out six pieces which have different shades. (These can be of different colours.)
❖ Match the pieces of magazine picture against the shade strip at the bottom of this page.
❖ Stick the pieces on to another sheet of paper in order, from darkest to lightest.
❖ Write the shade number under each on.

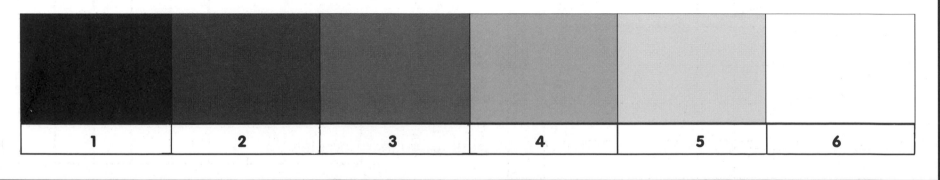

| 1 | 2 | 3 | 4 | 5 | 6 |

142

Measuring area

❧ Which leaf has the largest area? To find out, count the square centimetres. What will you do about the bits of square?

Area of leaf is about _____ cm²

Area of leaf is about _____ cm²

❧ Draw round some leaves on the grid below and find out their areas in square centimetres.

Wheat seedlings

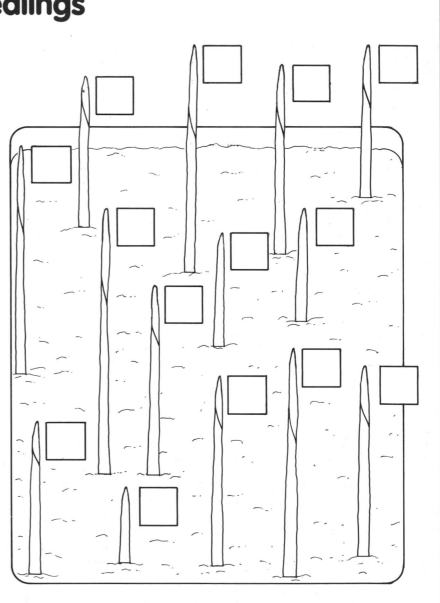

Wheat seedlings

Kulbinder is growing wheat plants in a plastic tub.
These are his seedlings after seven days.

♣ Measure the height of each seedling in centimetres.
♣ Write its height into the box next to each seedling.
♣ Now complete this table of results.

Height (cm)	7	6	5	4	3	2	1
Number of seedlings of that height							

♣ Draw a graph on the grid to show these results.
♣ What do you notice about your graph?

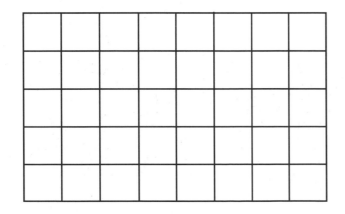